All-Time Favorites

Contents

HAL•LEONARD® CORPORATION

7777 W. BLUEMOUND RD. P.O. BOX 13819 MILWAUKEE, WI 53213

LOWREY

Alley Cat Song

Registration: *FULL 'N BRILLIANT*

Words by Jack Harlen
Music by Frank Bjorn

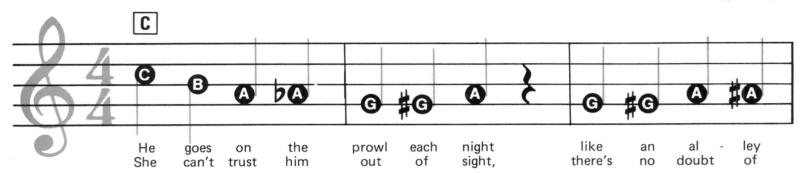

He goes on the prowl each night, like an al - ley
She can't trust him out of sight, there's no doubt of

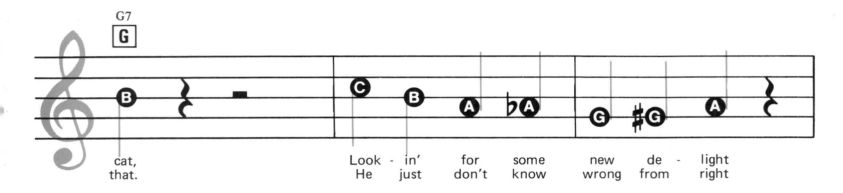

cat,
that.
Look - in' for some new de - light
He just don't know wrong from right

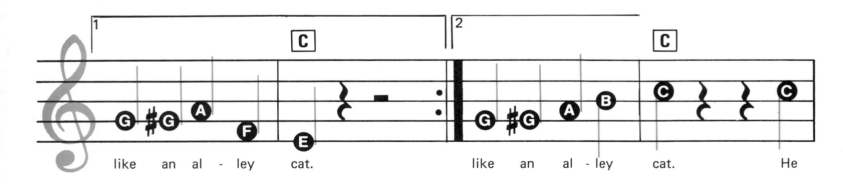

like an al - ley cat.
like an al - ley cat. He

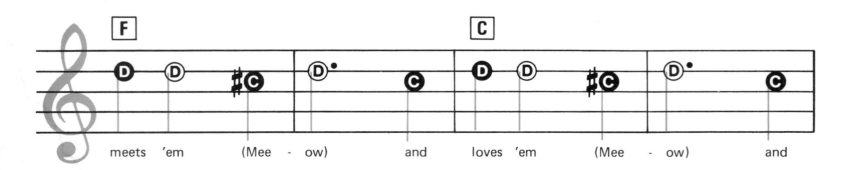

meets 'em (Mee - ow) and loves 'em (Mee - ow) and

3

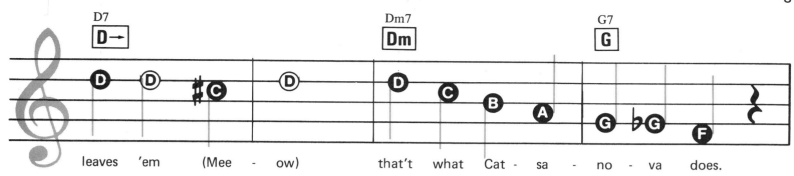

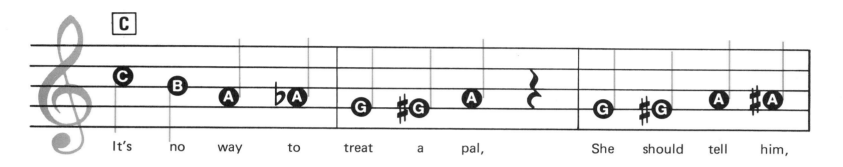

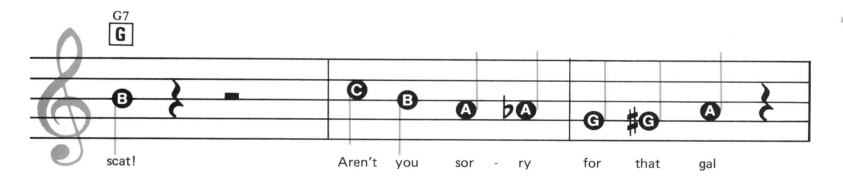

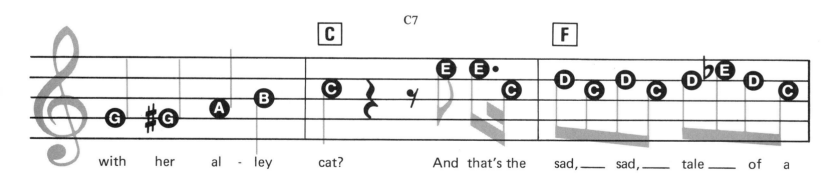

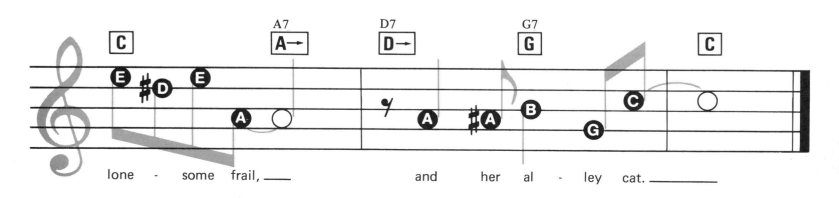

Hey, Mr. Banjo

Registration: *BRILLIANT SOLO*

By Freddy Morgan
and Norman Malkin

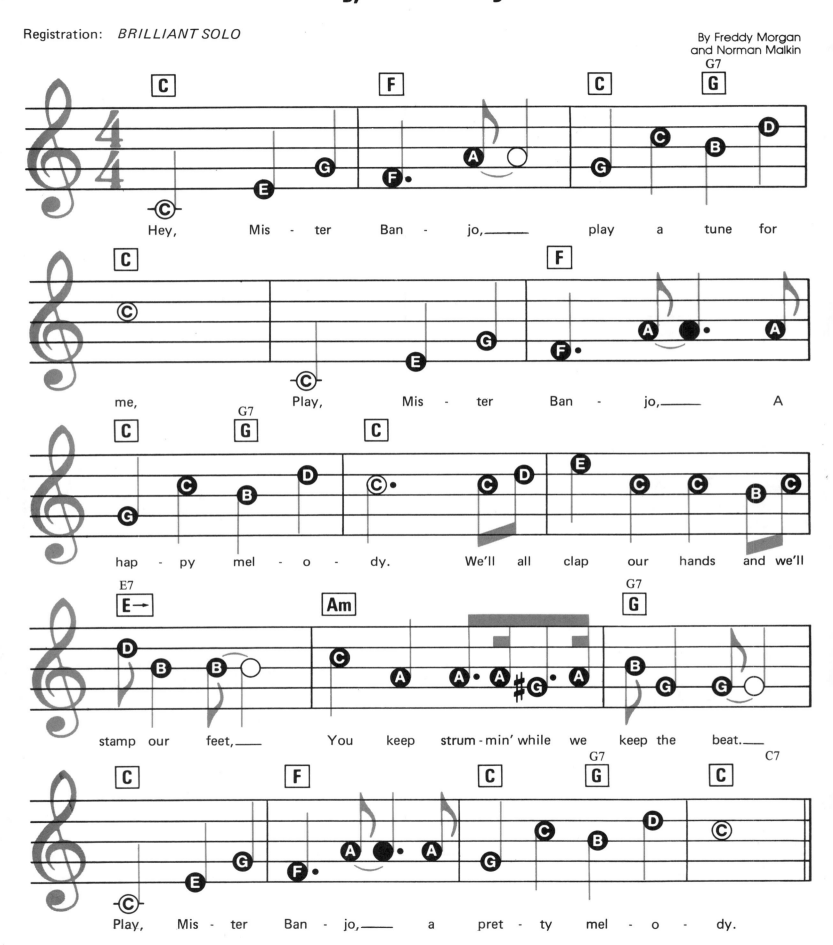

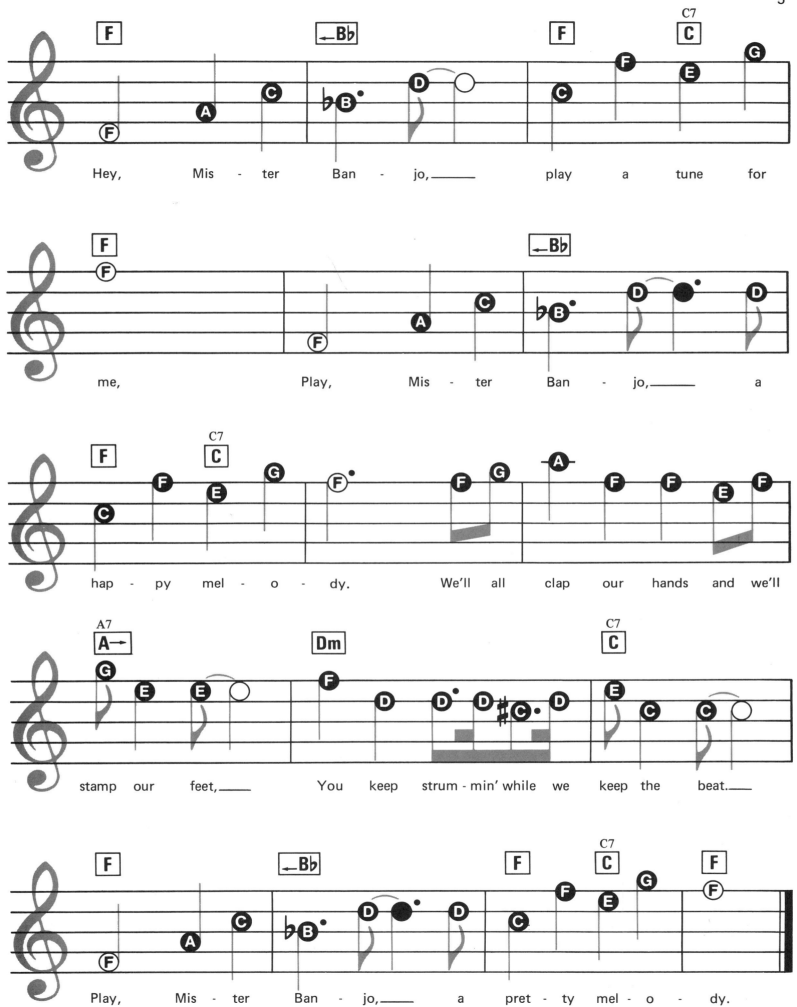

The Hawaiian Wedding Song

Registration: *FULL 'N MELLOW*

Use Glide as indicated by ✱
for Hawaiian Guitar "slide."

English Words by Al Hoffman and Dick Manning
Hawaiian Words and Music by Charles E. King

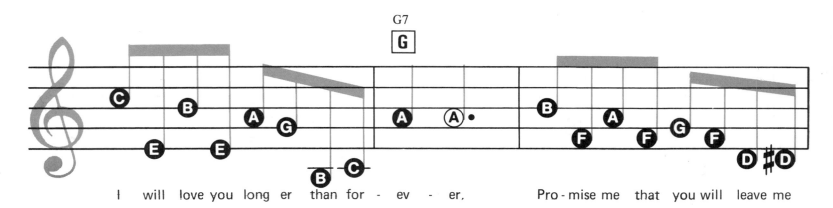

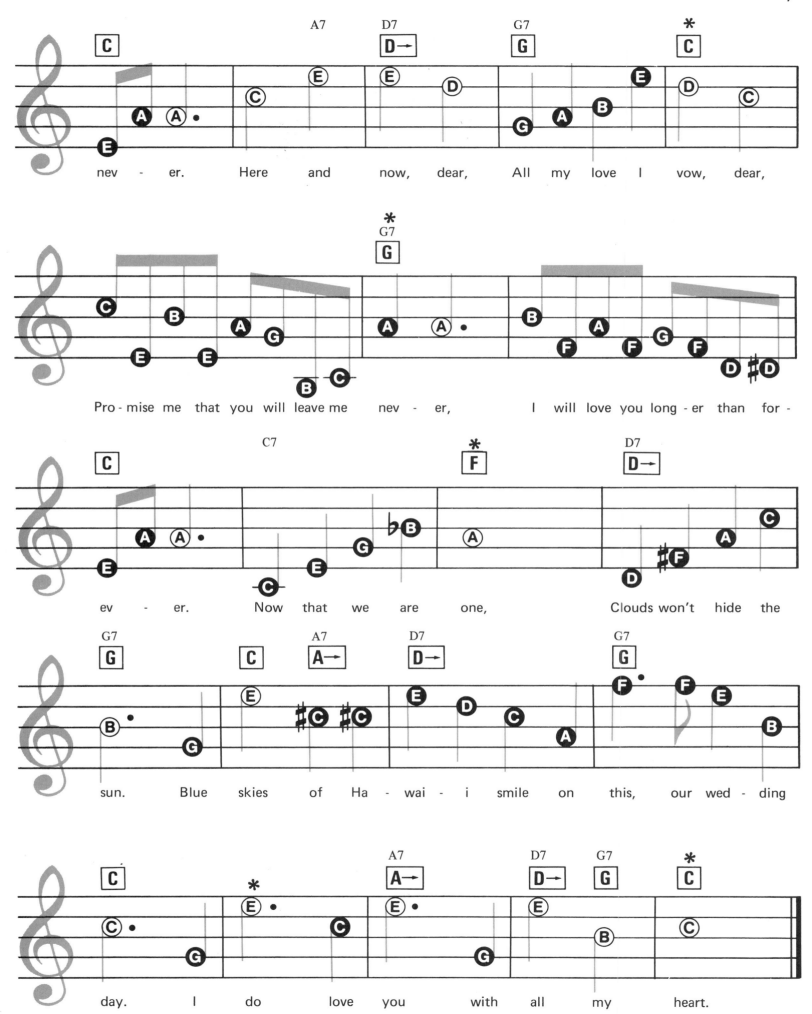

8

Green, Green Grass Of Home

Registration: *FULL 'N MELLOW*
or *POP ORGAN*

SP.92   SCROLL

Words and Music by
Curly Putman

The old home-town looks the same, as I step down from the
old house is still standing, Tho' the paint is cracked and

train,_____ And there to greet me is my Ma - ma_____ and
dry,_____ And there's that old oak tree_____ that I used_____ to

Pa - pa; Down the road I look and
play on; Down the road I walk with

there runs Ma - ry,} Hair of gold and lips like cher - ries, it's
my sweet Ma - ry,}

9

Twilight Time

Registration: *SOFT SOLO*

Lyric by Buck Ram
Music by Morty Nevins and Al Nevins

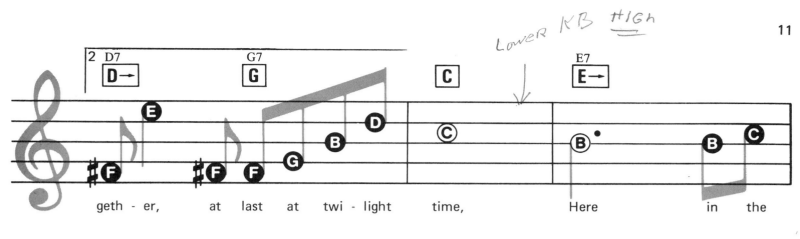

geth - er, at last at twi - light time, Here in the

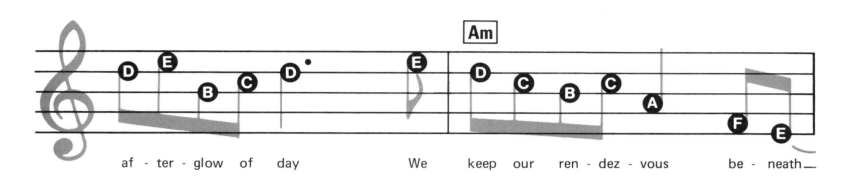

af - ter - glow of day We keep our ren - dez - vous be - neath

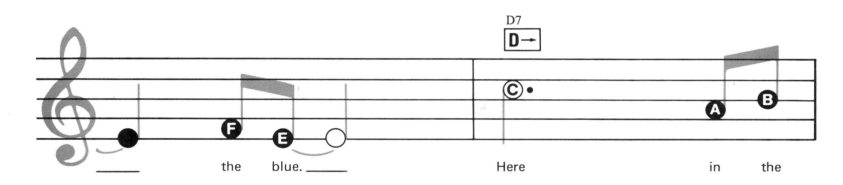

the blue. Here in the

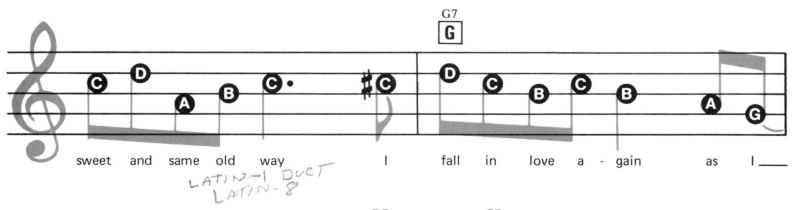

sweet and same old way I fall in love a - gain as I

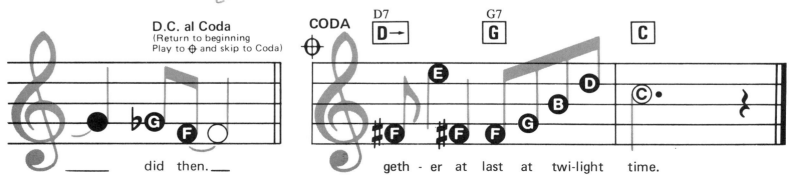

D.C. al Coda
(Return to beginning
Play to ⊕ and skip to Coda)

did then.

CODA

geth - er at last at twi - light time.

Any Time

STICK

Words and Music by
Herbert Happy Lawson

Registration: *BIG 'N BOLD*

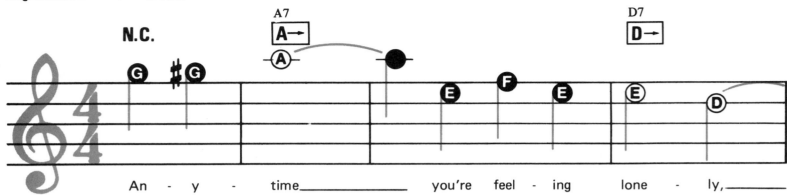

An - y - time_____ you're feel - ing lone - ly,_____

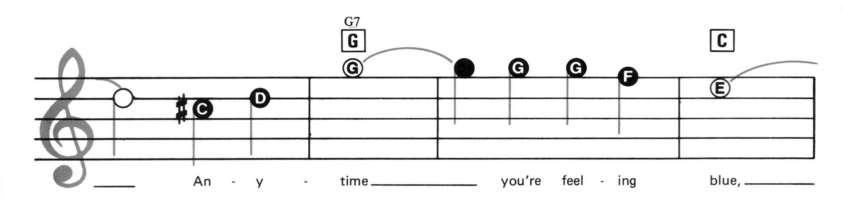

____ An - y - time_____ you're feel - ing blue,_____

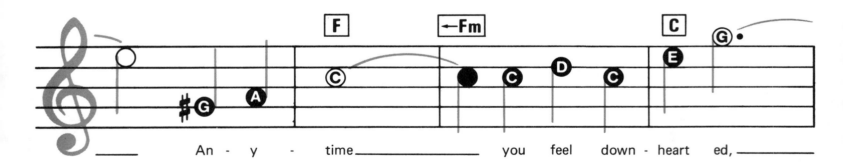

____ An - y - time_____ you feel down - heart ed,

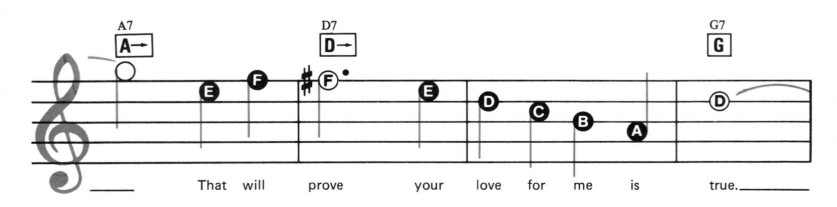

____ That will prove your love for me is true._____

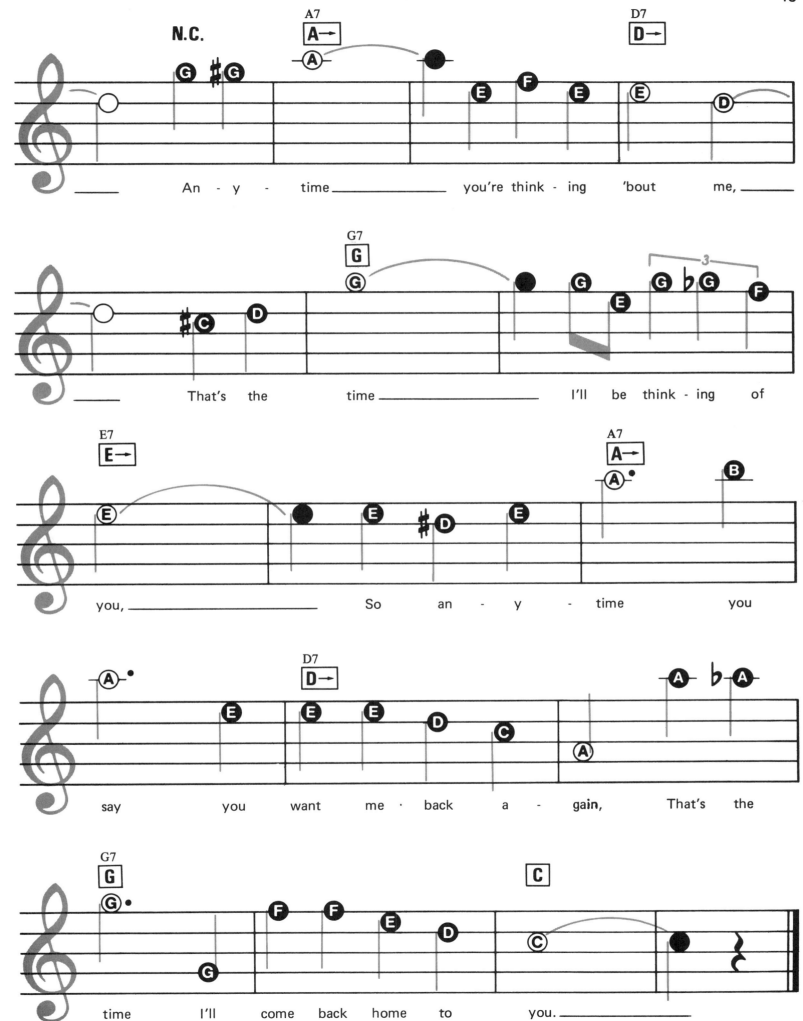

14

I'm Gettin' Sentimental Over You

Registration: *SOFT SOLO*

Use Glide as indicated by asterisk *

By Washington, Bassman

Nev - er thought I'd fall, But now I hear love call, I'm get - tin' sen - ti - ment - al o - ver you, Things you say and do, Just thrill me through and through, I'm get - tin' sen - ti - ment - al o - ver you, I thought I was

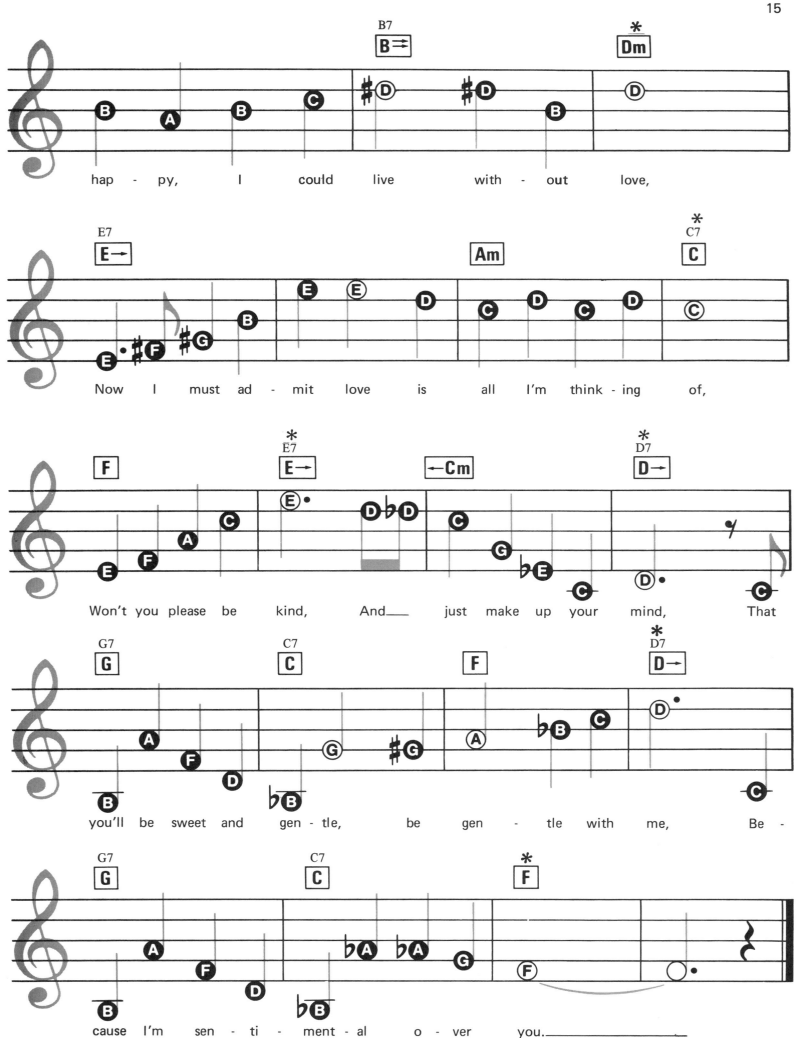

Mood Indigo

SATIN LADY
P 10
OR
SERENADE
P-6

Registration: *SOFT SOLO*

SCROLL
104

By Duke Ellington, Albany Bigard
and Irving Mills

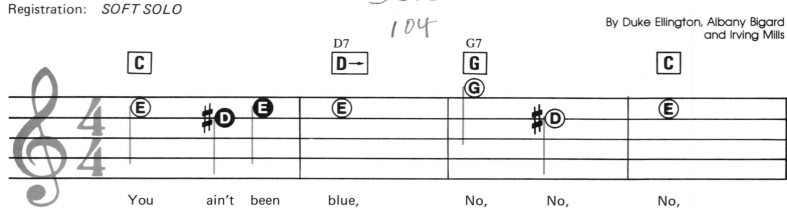

You ain't been blue, No, No, No,

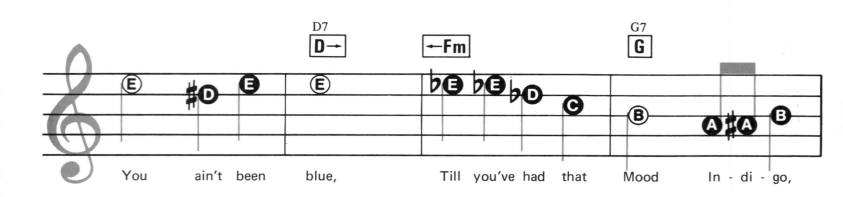

You ain't been blue, Till you've had that Mood In - di - go,

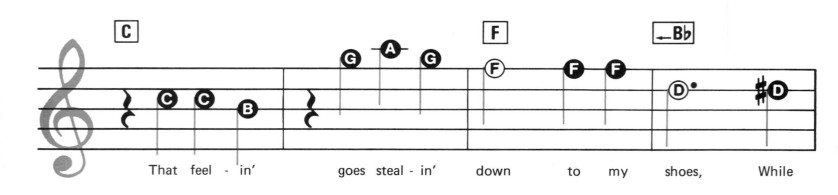

That feel - in' goes steal - in' down to my shoes, While

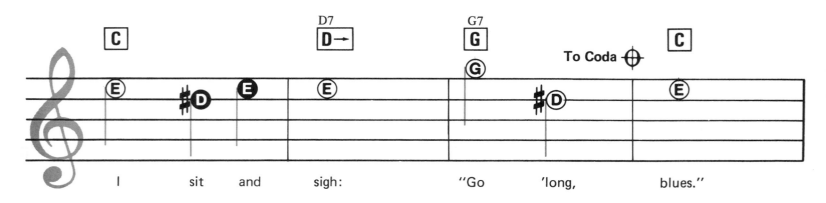

I sit and sigh: "Go 'long, blues."

Anniversary Song

Registration: *FULL 'N MELLOW*

By Al Jolson
and Saul Chaplin

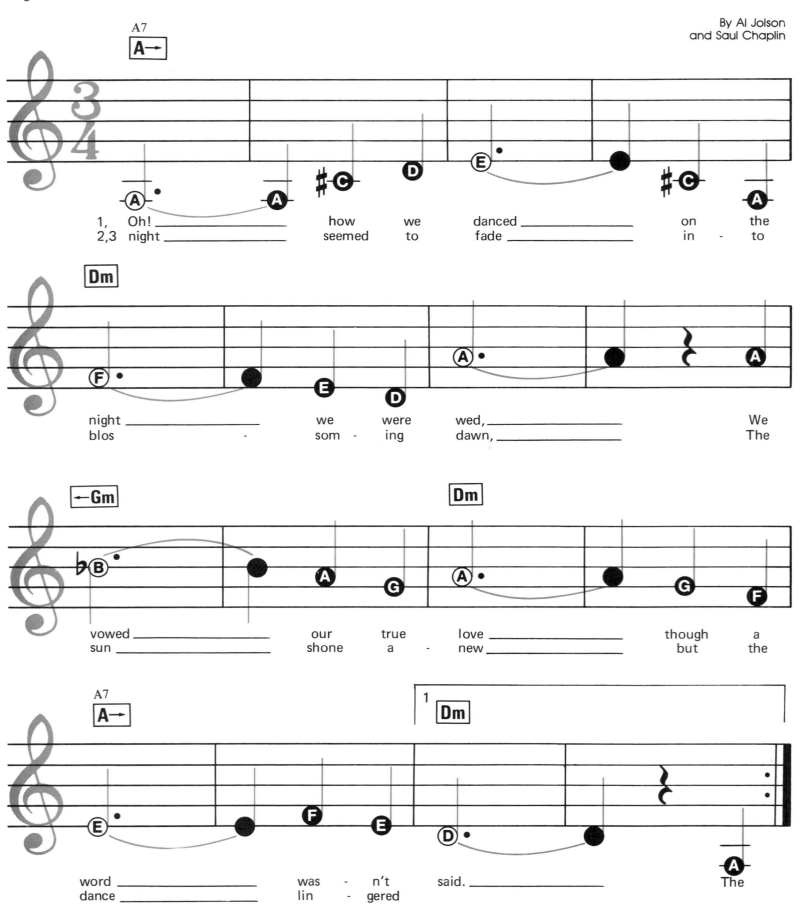

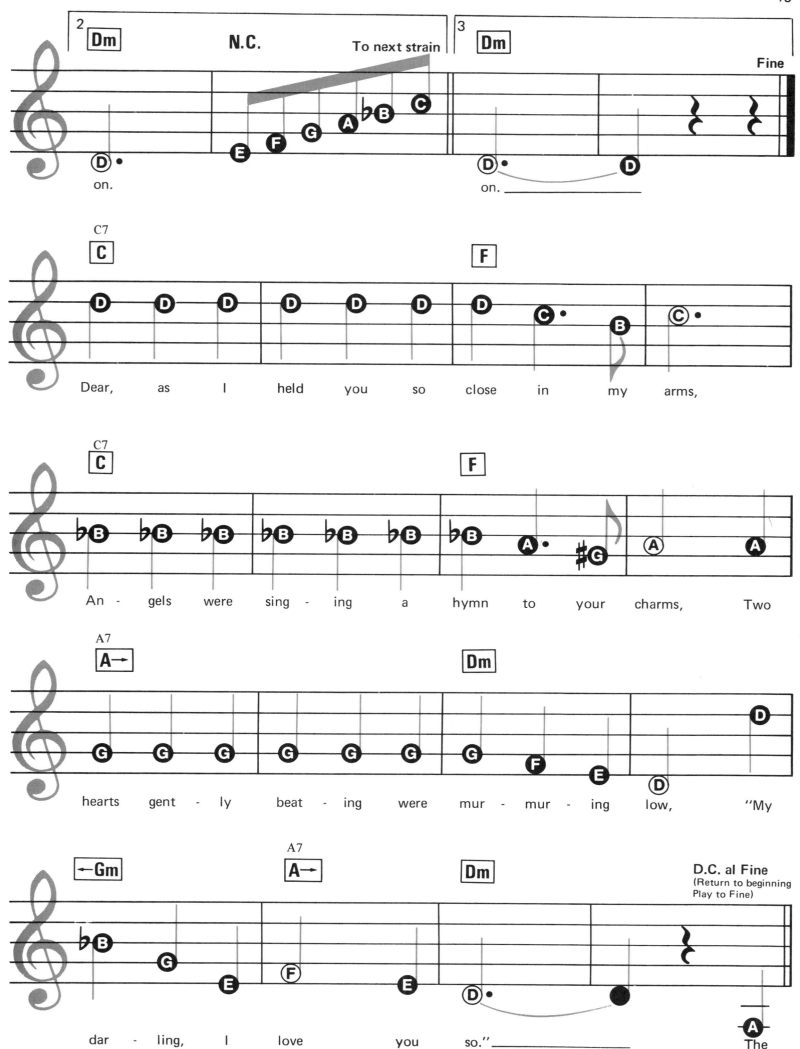

Melody Of Love

Registration: *SOFT SOLO*

Lyric by Tom Glazer
Music by H. Engelmann

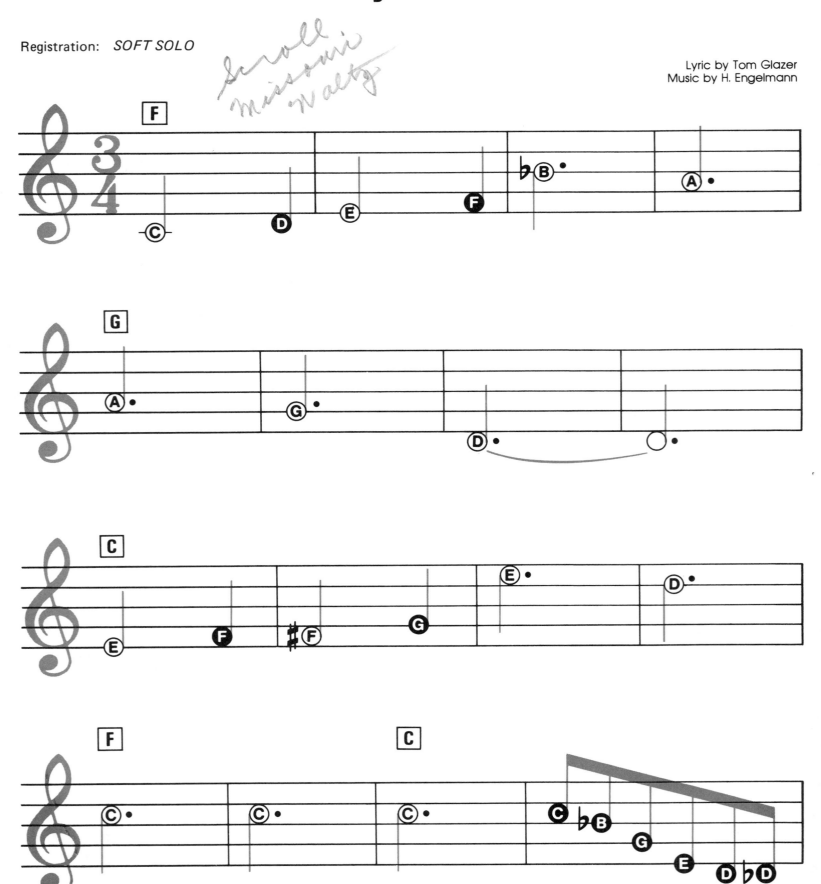

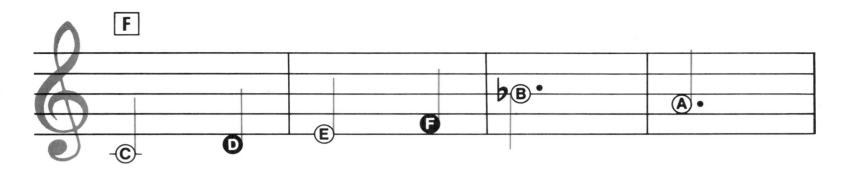

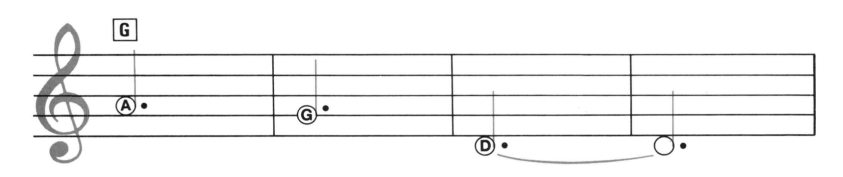

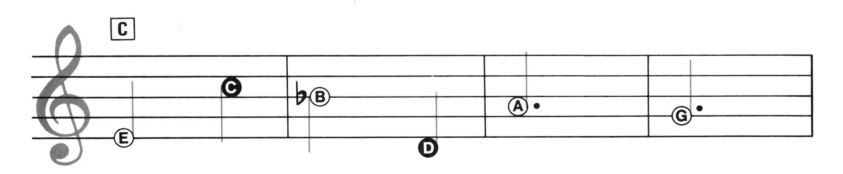

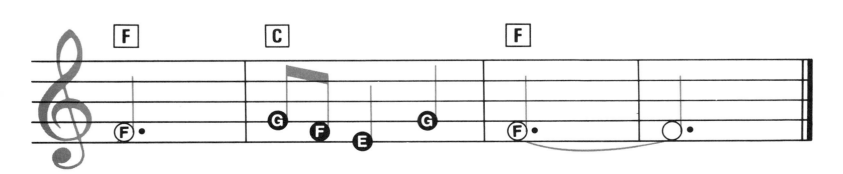

The Third Man Theme

Registration: *BRILLIANT SOLO*

Words by Walter Lord
Based on music composed and
arranged by Anton Karas

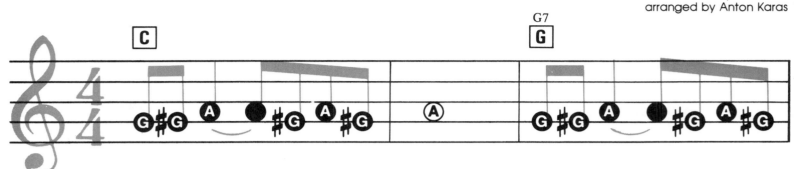

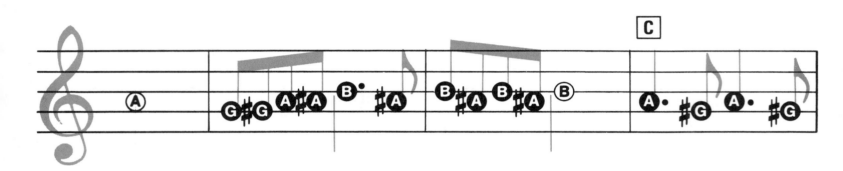

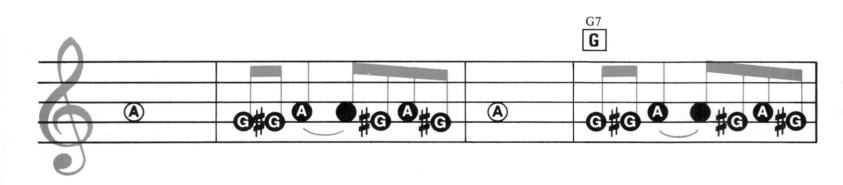

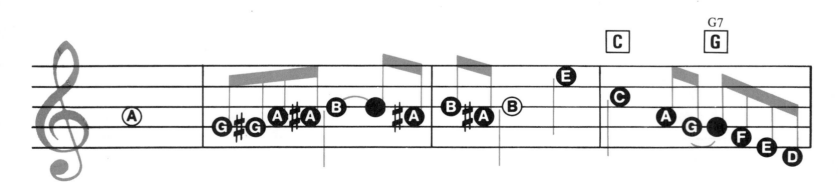

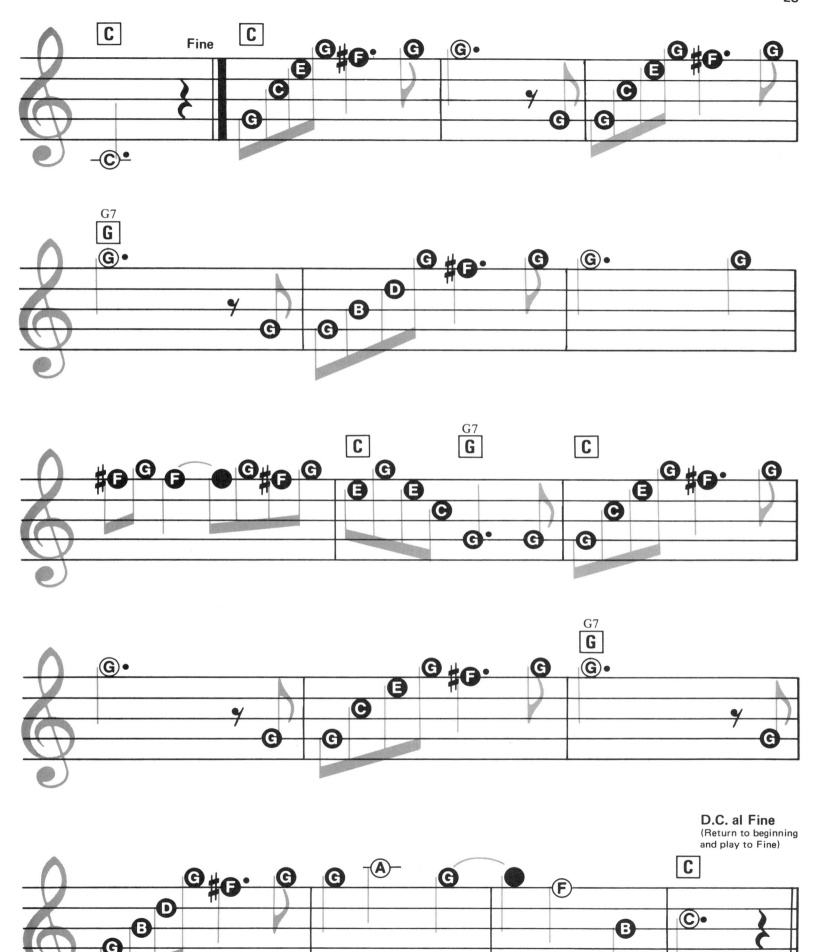

Under Paris Skies
(Sous Le Ciel De Paris)

Registration: *SOFT SOLO*

English Words by Kim Gannon
French Words by Jean Drejac
Music by Hubert Giraud

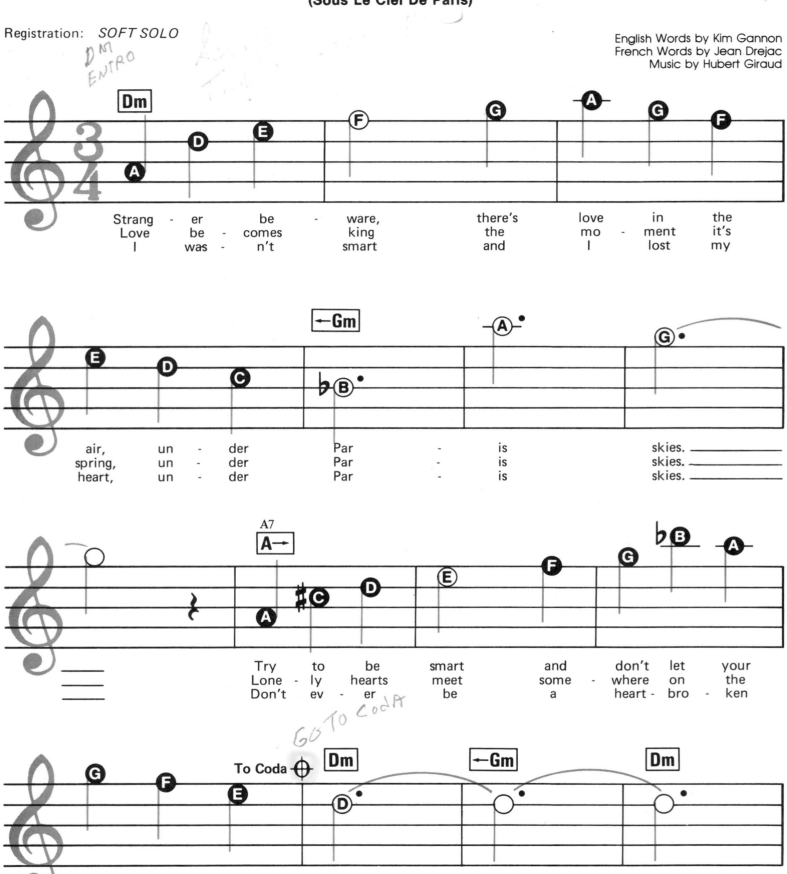

What Have They Done To My Song, Ma?

Registration: *BRILLIANT SOLO*

Words and Music by
Melanie Safka

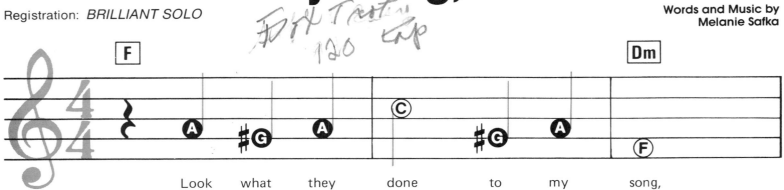

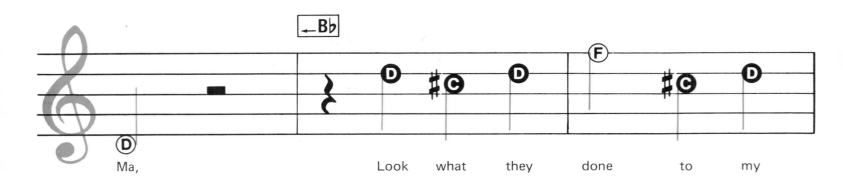

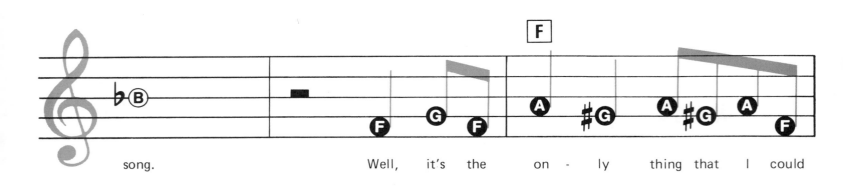

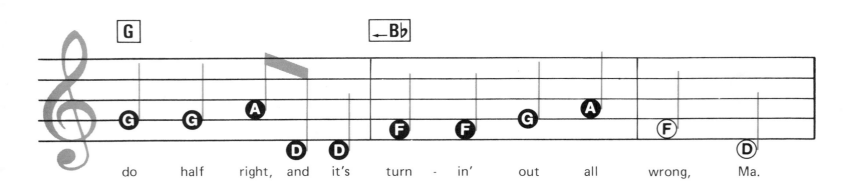

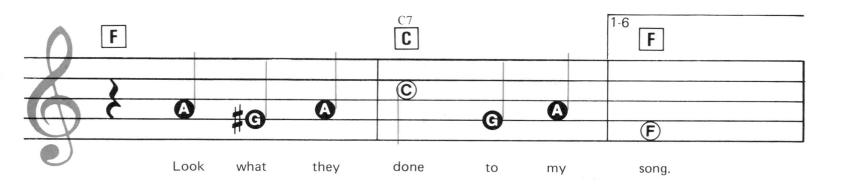

Look   what   they   done   to   my   song.

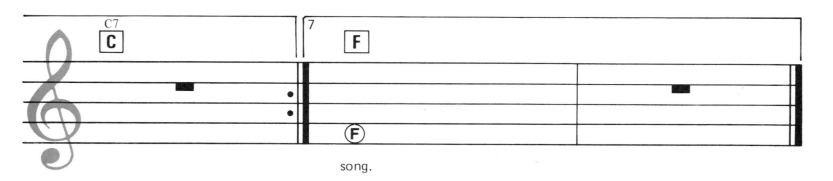

song.

Verse

2. Look what they done to my brain, Ma
   Look what they done to my brain,
   Well, they picked it like a chicken bone
   And I think I'm half insane, Ma,
   Look what they done to my song.

3. I wish I could find a good book to live in,
   Wish I could find a good book.
   Well, if I could find a real good book,
   I'd never have to come out and look,
   At what they done to my song.

4. But maybe it'll all be alright, Ma,
   Maybe it'll all be o.k.
   Well, if the people are buying tears
   I'll be rich some day, Ma.
   Look what they done to my song.

5. Ils ont changé ma chanson, Ma
   Ils ont changé ma chanson.
   C'est la seule chose que je peux faire
   Et ce n'est pas bon, Ma.
   Ils ont changé ma chanson.

6. Look what they done to my song, Ma
   Look what they done to my song.
   Well, they tied it up in a plastic bag
   And turned it upside down, Ma.
   Look what they done to my song.

7. Look what they done to my song, Ma
   Look what they done to my song.
   It's the only thing I could do alright,
   And they turned it upside down.
   Look what they done to my song.

Star Dust

Registration: *SOFT SOLO*

Words by Mitchell Parish
Music by Hoagy Carmichael

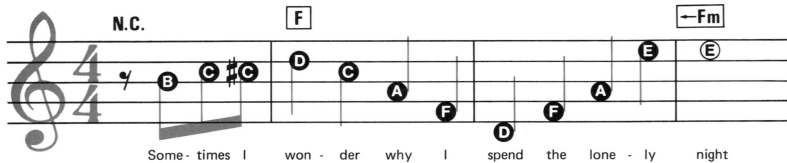

Some - times I won - der why I spend the lone - ly night

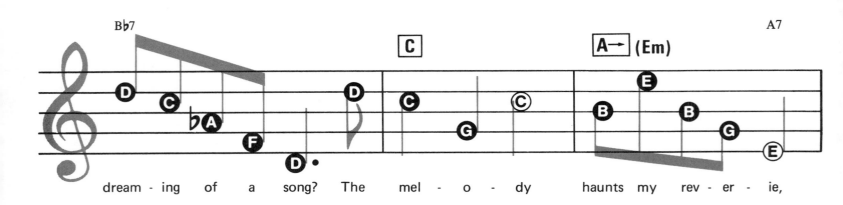

dream - ing of a song? The mel - o - dy haunts my rev - er - ie,

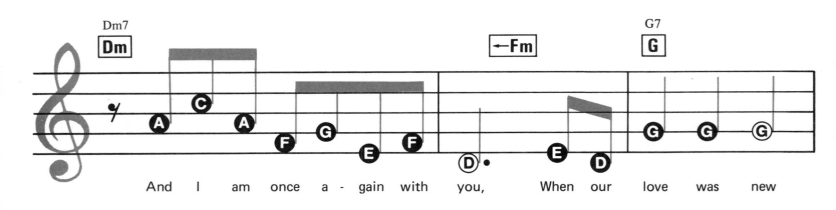

And I am once a - gain with you, When our love was new

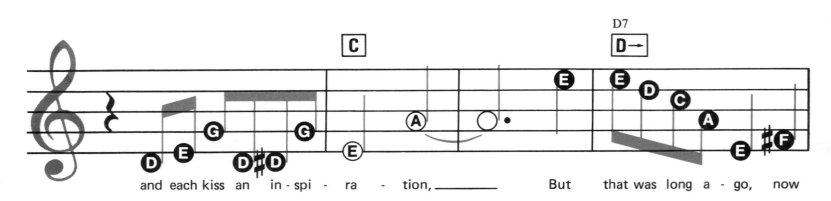

and each kiss an in - spi - ra - tion, _____ But that was long a - go, now

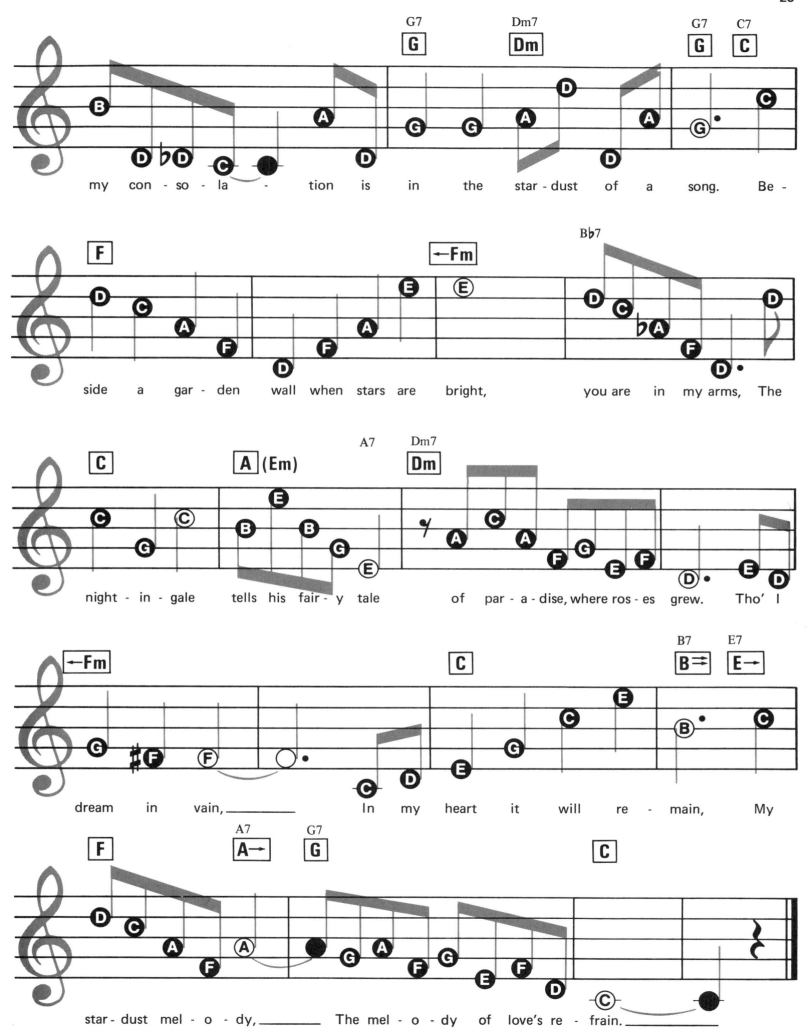

Yesterday

Registration: *FULL 'N' BRILLIANT*

Words and Music by John Lennon &
Paul McCartney

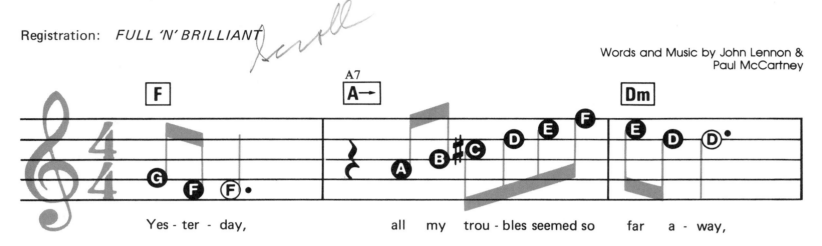

Yes - ter - day, all my trou - bles seemed so far a - way,

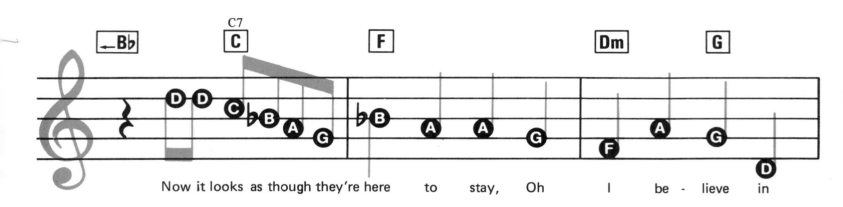

Now it looks as though they're here to stay, Oh I be - lieve in

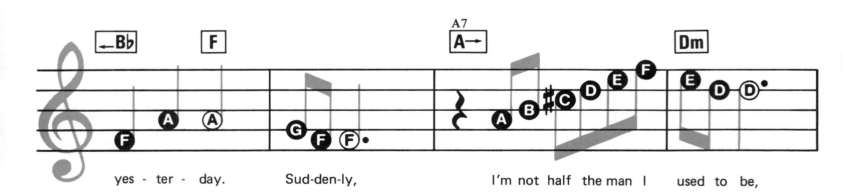

yes - ter - day. Sud - den - ly, I'm not half the man I used to be,

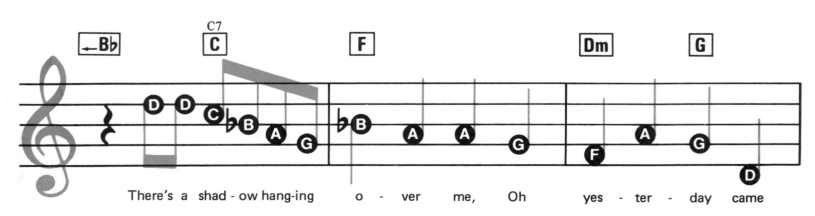

There's a shad - ow hang - ing o - ver me, Oh yes - ter - day came

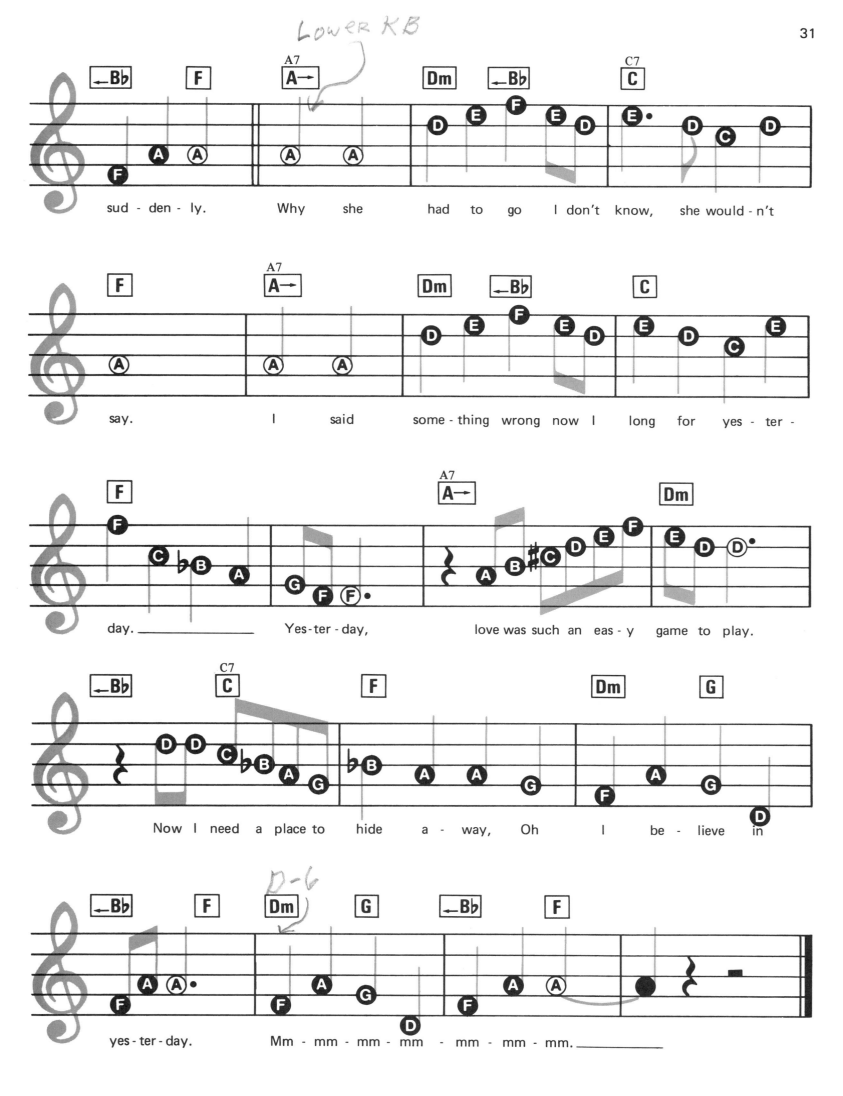

On The Sunny Side Of The Street

Registration: *BIG 'N BOLD*

Lyric by Dorothy Fields
Music by Jimmy McHugh

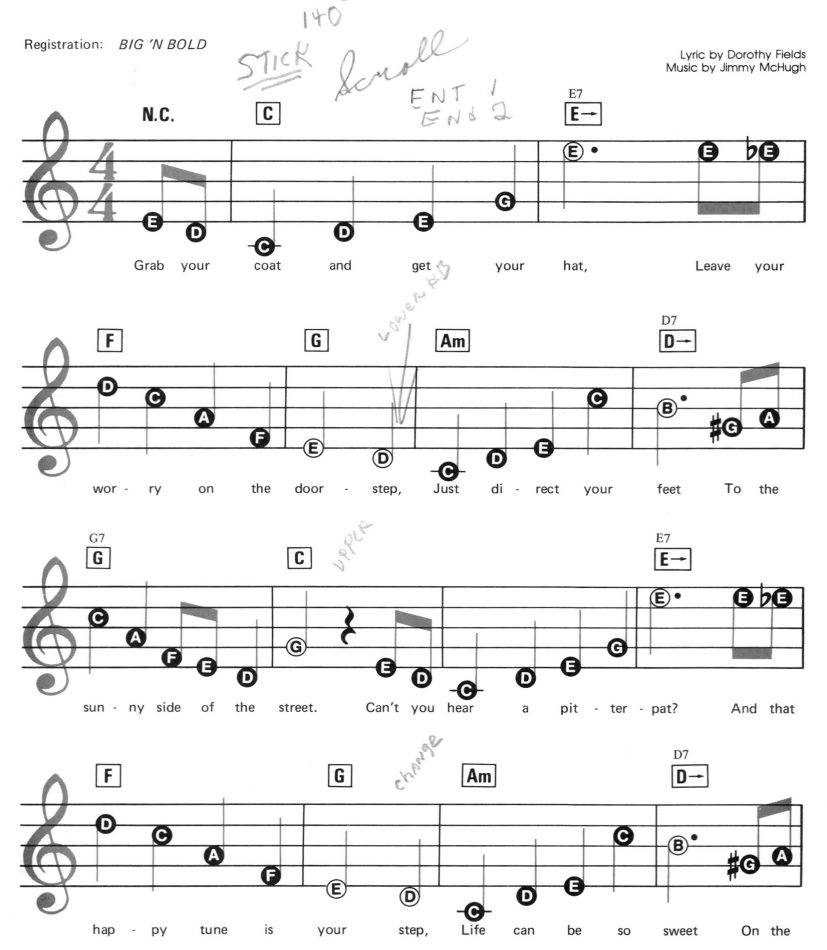

33

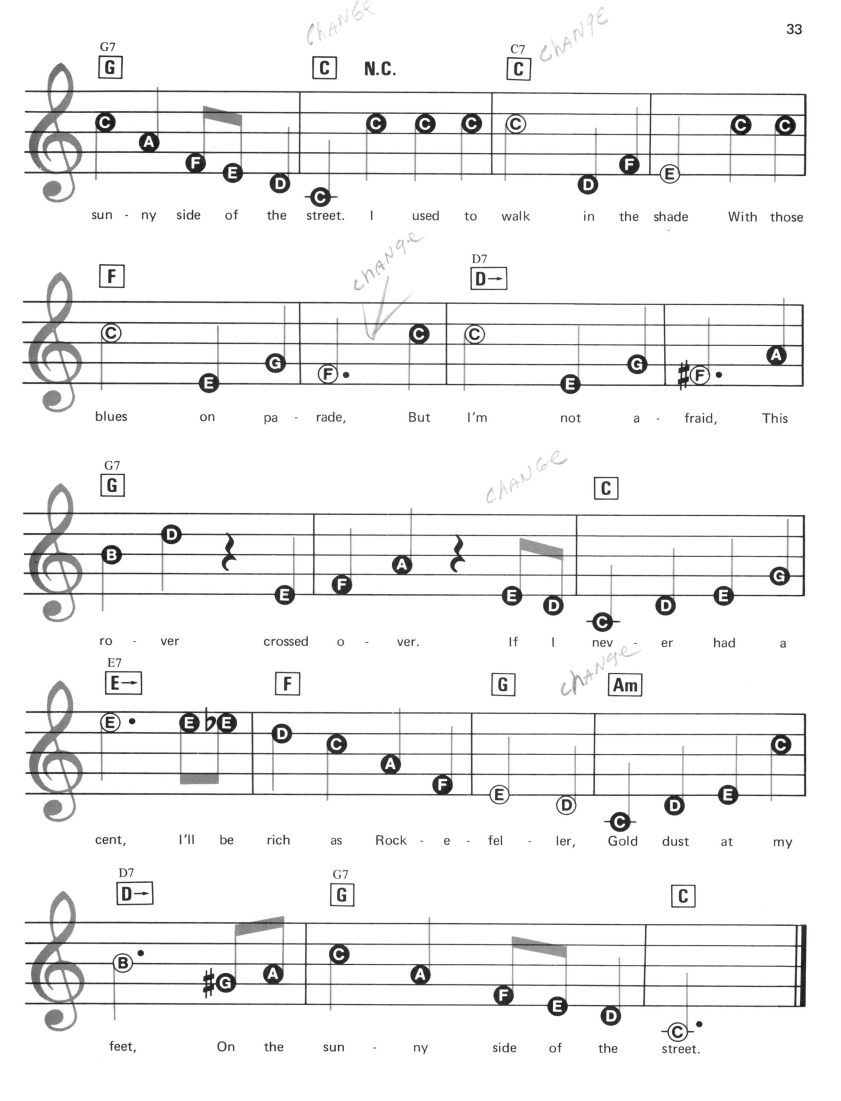

Whistle While You Work

(From Walt Disney's "SNOW WHITE AND THE SEVEN DWARFS")

Registration: *FULL 'N' MELLOW*

Words by Larry Morey
Music by Frank Churchill

Just whis - tle while you work. (Whistle) _____

_____ Put on that grin and start right in, To

whis - tle loud and long. Just hum a mer - ry tune. (Hum) _____

Just do your best, then take a rest, And

Blue Velvet

Registration: *FULL 'N MELLOW*

By Bernie Wayne
and Lee Morris

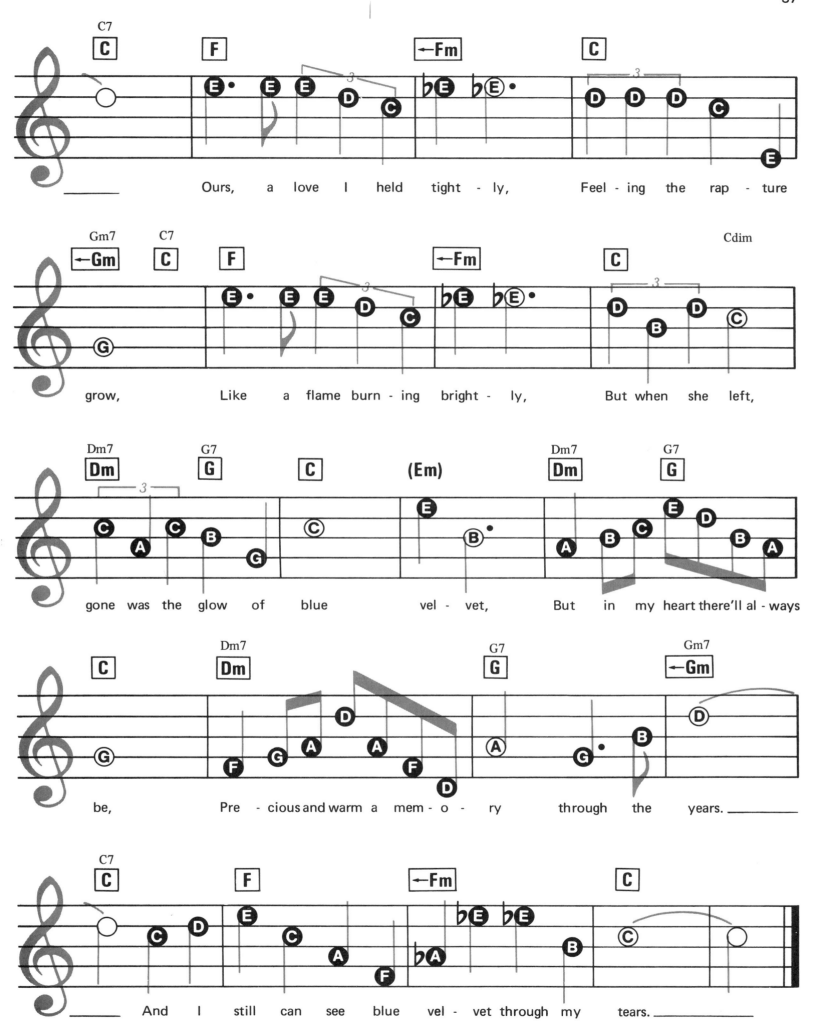

King Of The Road

Registration: *BIG 'N BOLD*

By Roger Miller

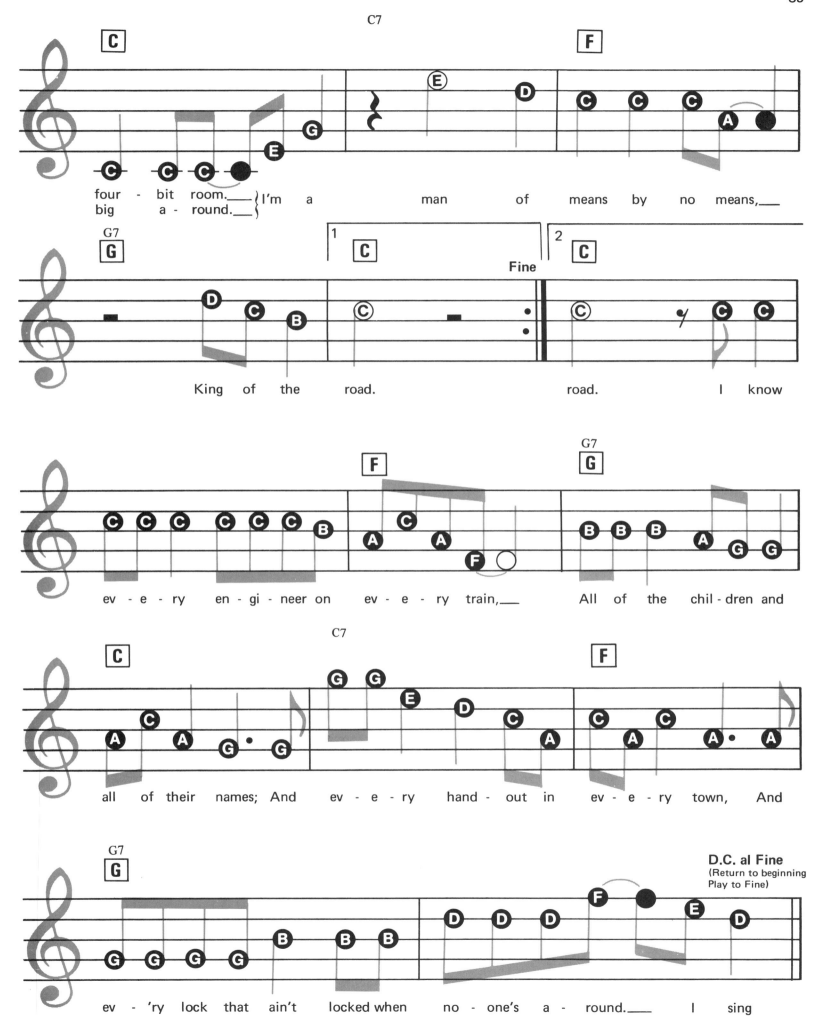

The Girl From Ipanema
(Garôta De Ipanema)

Original Words by Vinicius De Moraes
English Words by Norman Gimbel
Music by Antonio Carlos Jobim

Registration: *FULL 'N MELLOW*

1,3. Tall and tan and young and love-ly, the girl from I-pa-
2. When she walks she's like a sam-ba that swings so cool and

ne-ma goes walk-ing, and
sways___ so gen-tle, that} when she pass-es, each one she pass-es goes

"aah!"___

"aah!"___

Oh,___ but I watch her so sad-ly.___

How___ can I tell her I love her?___

41

Yes _____ I would give my heart glad - ly, _____

FX 2 MEASURES

_____ But each day when she walks to the sea, she

UPPER KB 5

D.C. al Coda
(Return to beginning
Play to ⊕ and
skip to Coda)

⊕ CODA

looks straight a - head, not at me.

when she pass - es I

E♭

smile, but she does - n't see.

She just does - n't

E♭

see. No, she does - n't see. _____

Sugar Blues

Registration: *BRILLIANT SOLO*

Words by Lucy Fletcher
Music by Clarence Williams

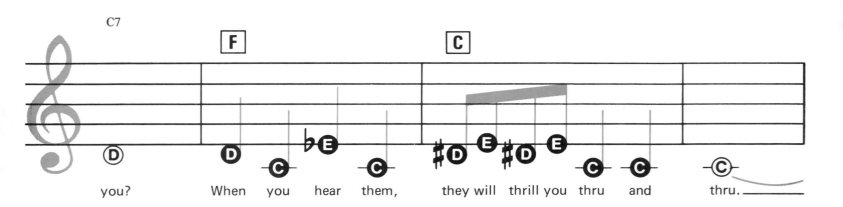

Have you heard these blues that I'm going to sing to

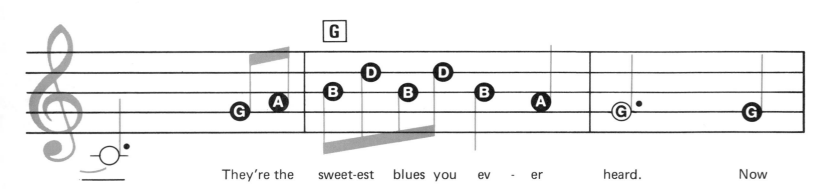

you? When you hear them, they will thrill you thru and thru.____

They're the sweet-est blues you ev - er heard. Now

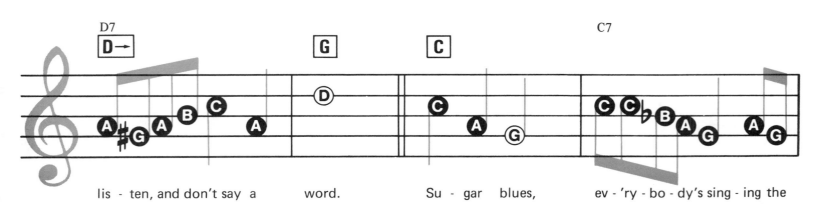

lis - ten, and don't say a word. Su - gar blues, ev - 'ry - bo - dy's sing - ing the

43

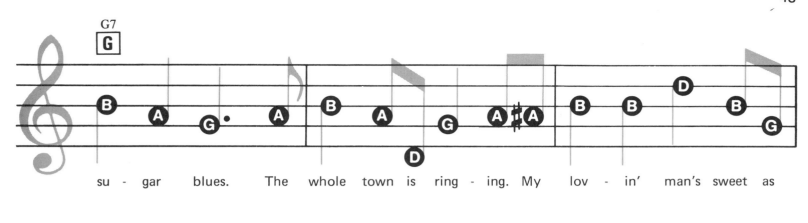

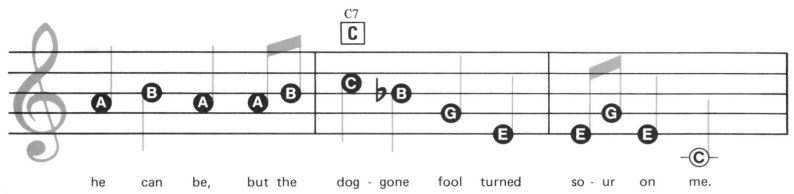

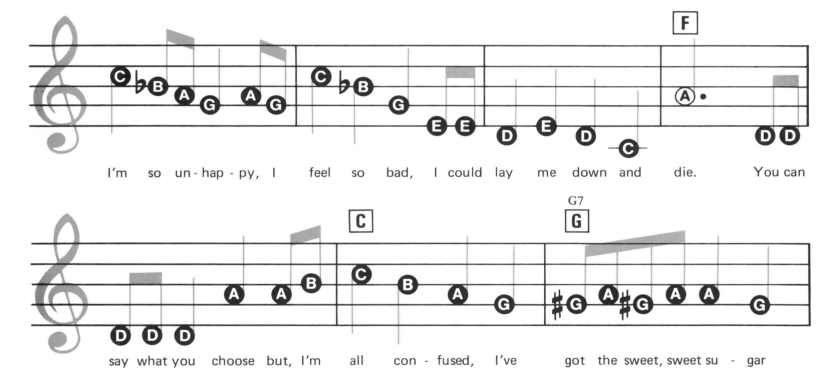

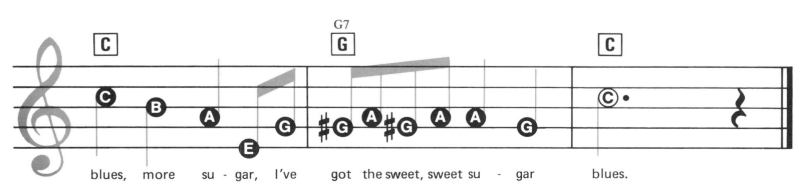

Autumn Leaves Tepo 85   (Foxtrot Variation SAmmy D Candy 95)

Honey

Registration: *SOFT SOLO*

FOX TROT TAP III

Words and Music by
Bobby Russell

See the tree, how big it's grown, but friend it has-n't been too long, it was-n't big,____
Then the first snow came and she ran out to brush the snow a-way so it would-n't die,____

____ I laughed at her and she got mad, the first day that she plant-ed it was
____ Came run-nin' in____ all ex-cit-ed, slipped and al-most hurt her-self, I

just a twig.____

laughed 'til I cried.____

And Hon-ey, I miss you ____ and I'm be-ing

45

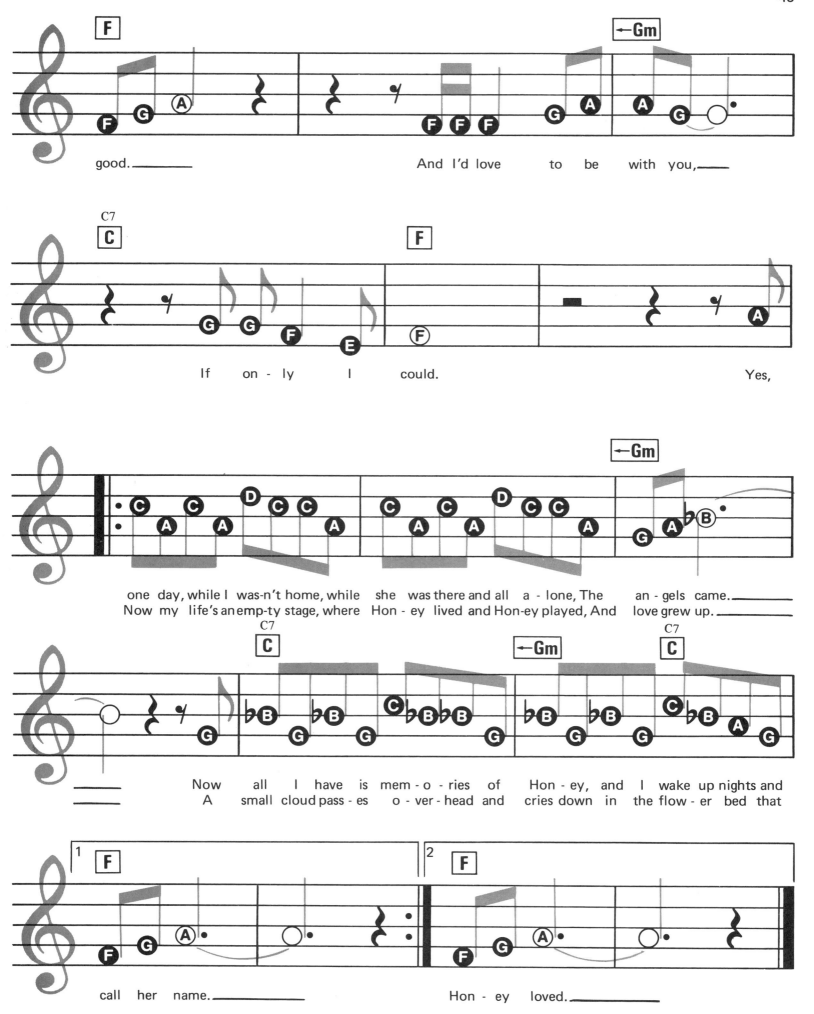

How Great Thou Art

Registration: CLASSICAL

By Stuart K. Hine

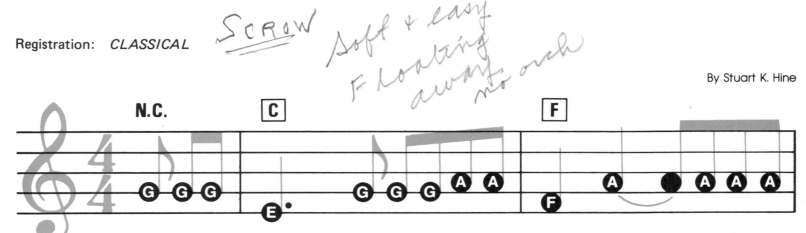

O Lord my God! When I in awe-some won - der_____ Con-si - der

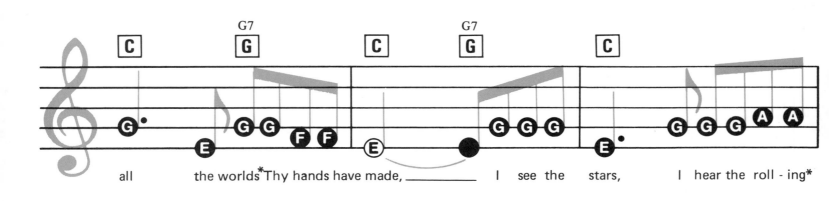

all the worlds*Thy hands have made,_____ I see the stars, I hear the roll - ing*

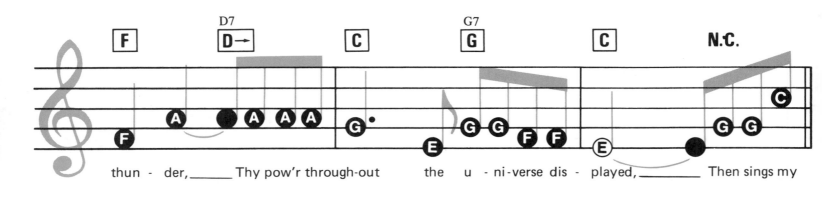

thun - der,_____ Thy pow'r through-out the u - ni-verse dis - played,_____ Then sings my

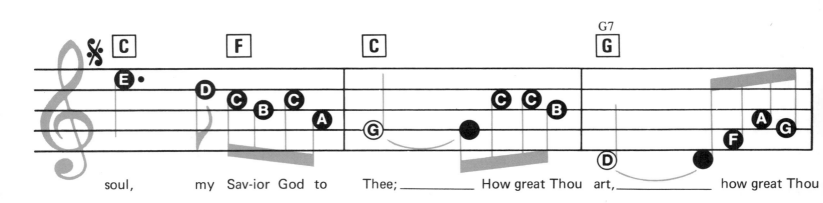

soul, my Sav-ior God to Thee;_____ How great Thou art,_____ how great Thou

*Author's original words are "works" and "mighty"

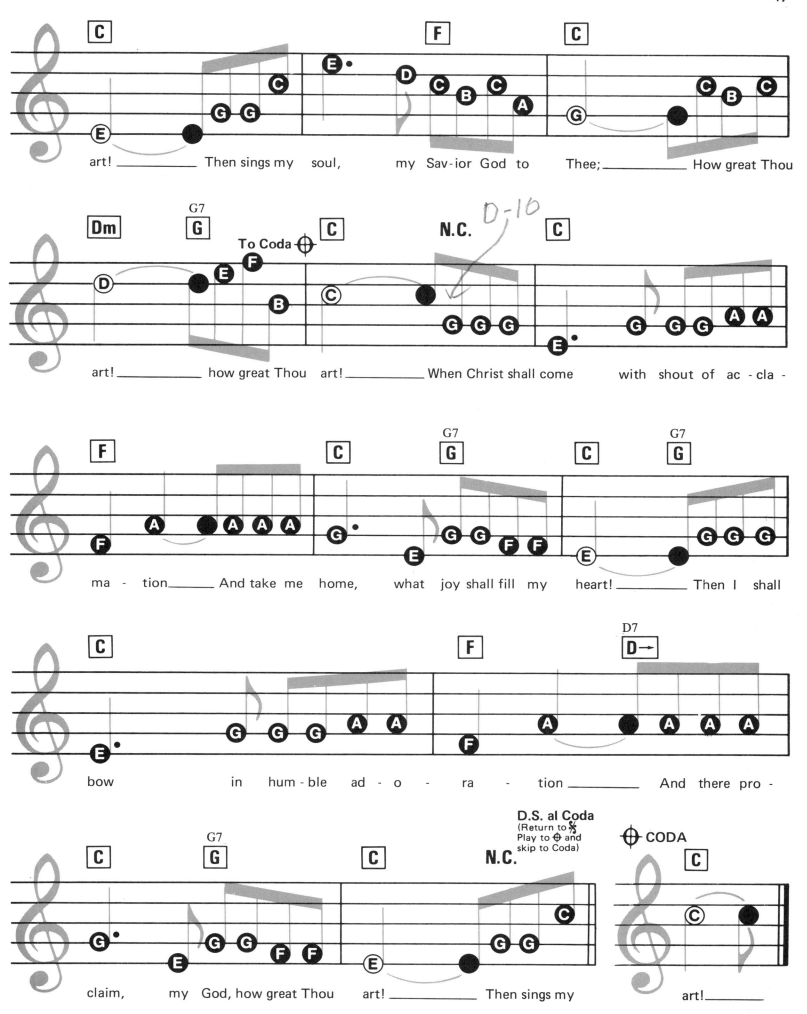

Blue Eyes

Registration: *SOFT SOLO*

Words and Music by Elton John
and Gary Osborne

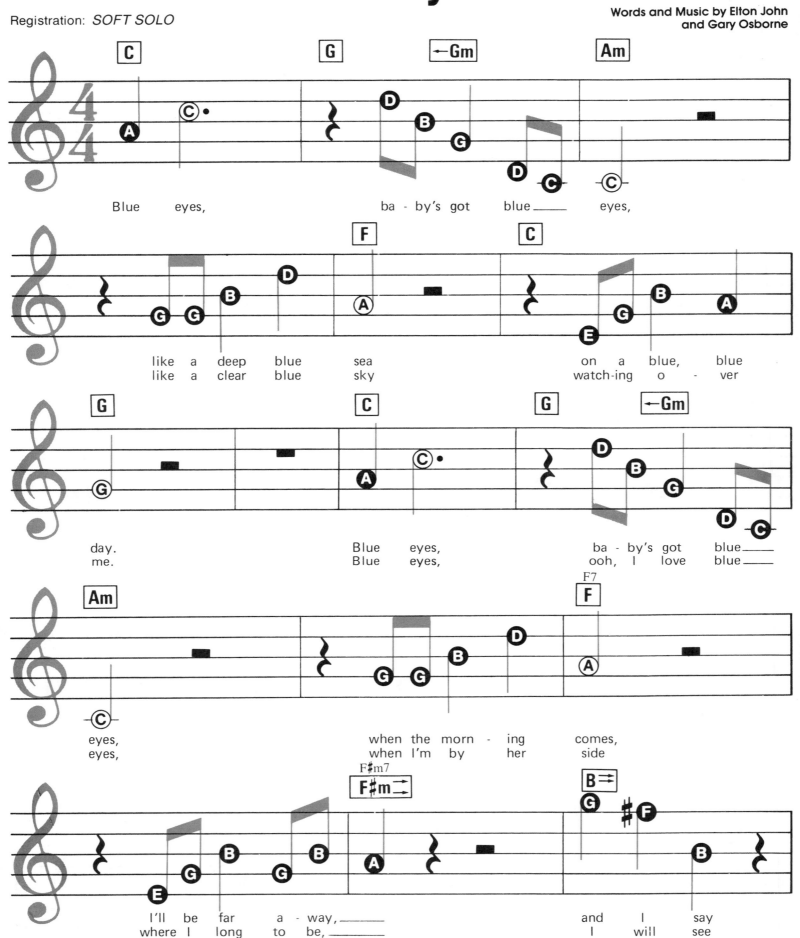

49

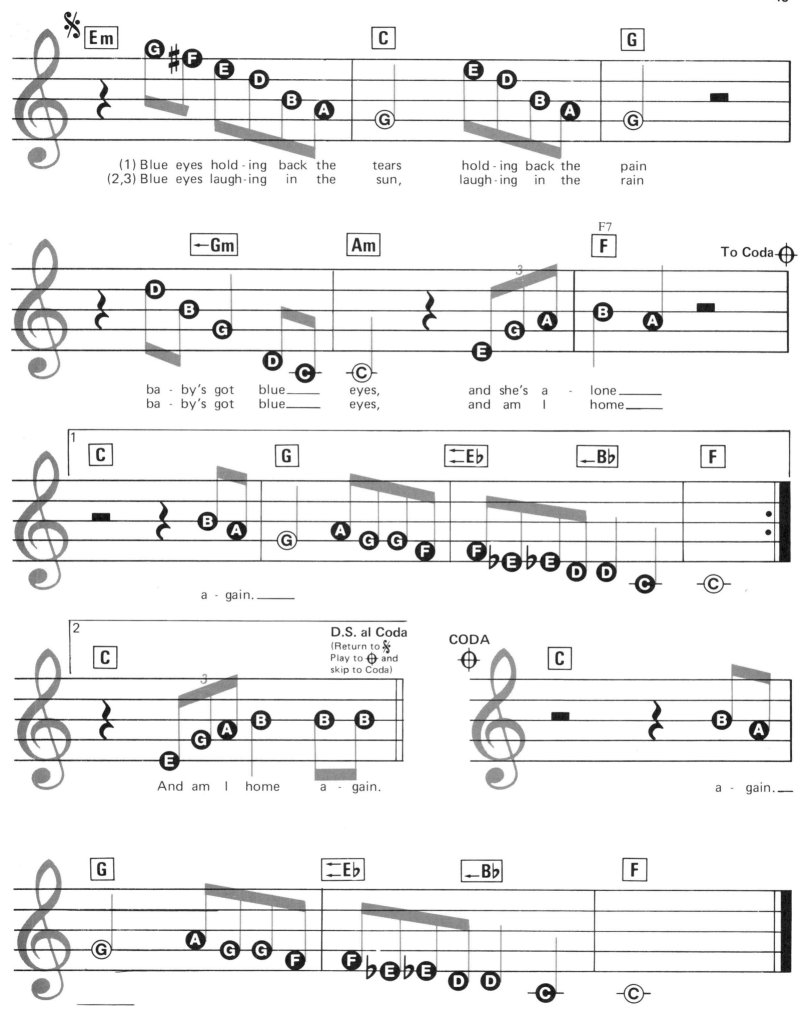

The Church's One Foundation

Registration: *CLASSICAL*

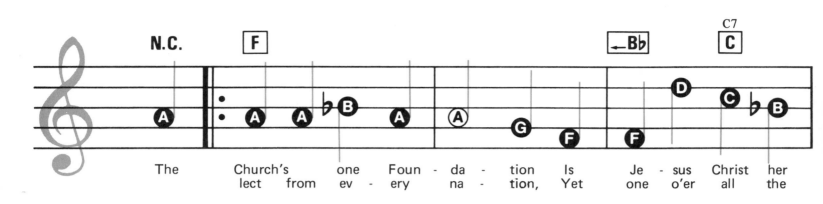

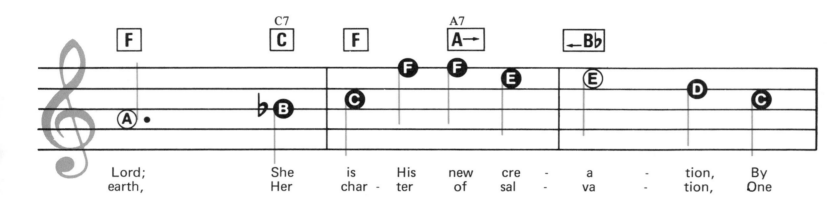

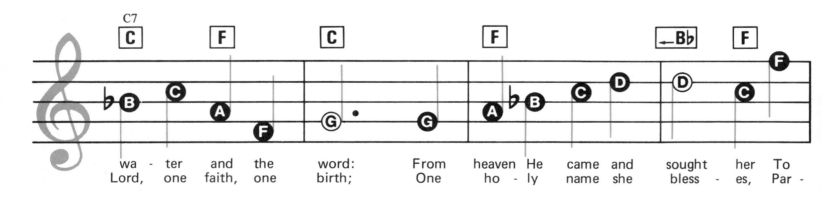

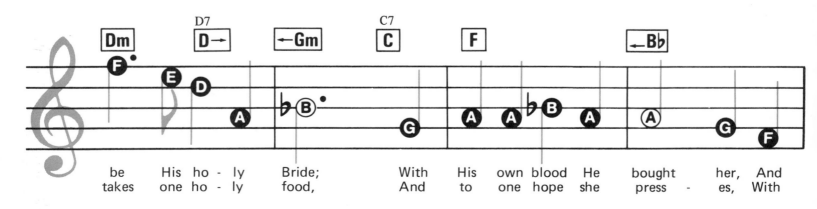

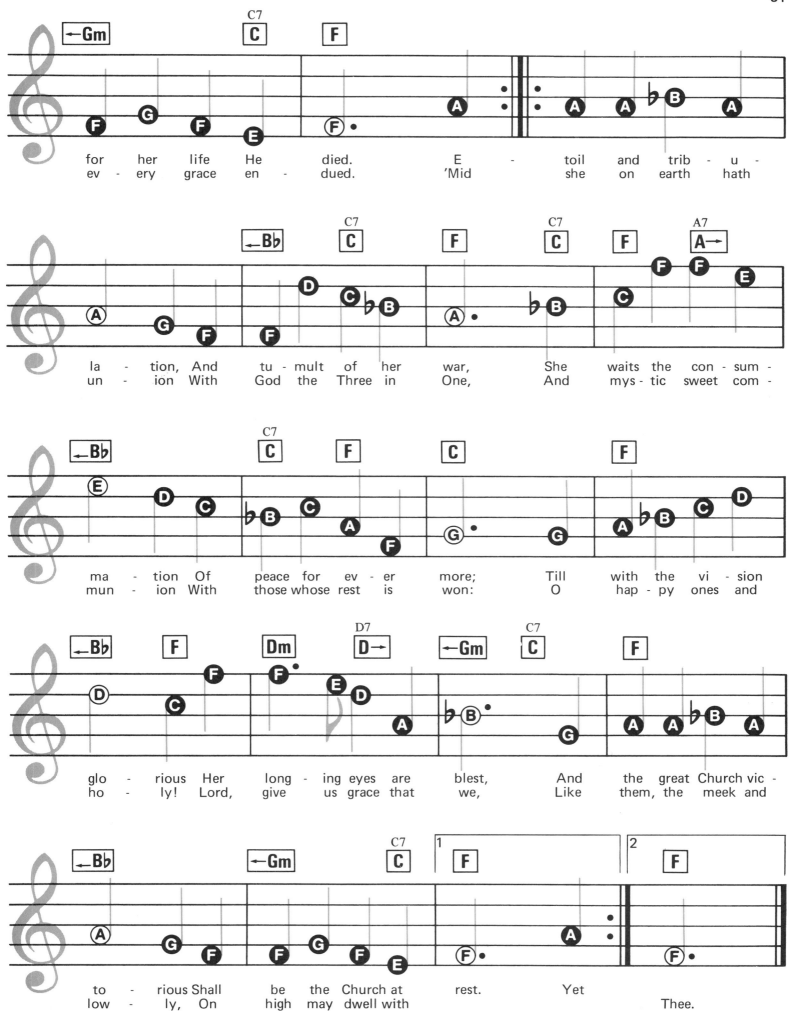

Shadow Dancing

Registration: *FULL 'N BRILLIANT*

Words and Music by
BARRY GIBB, ROBIN GIBB, MAURICE GIBB
and ANDY GIBB

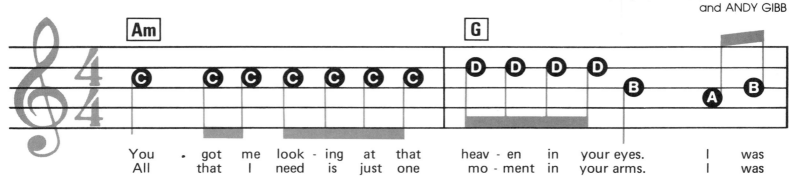

You got me look-ing at that heav-en in your eyes. I was
All that I need is just one mo-ment in your arms. I was

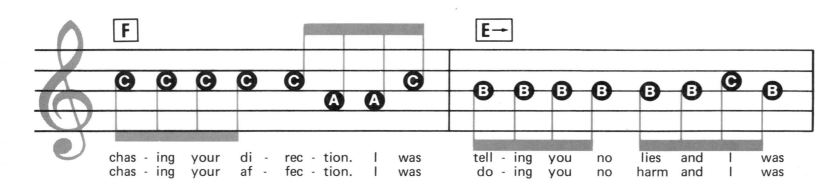

chas-ing your di-rec-tion. I was tell-ing you no lies and I was
chas-ing your af-fec-tion. I was do-ing you no harm and I was

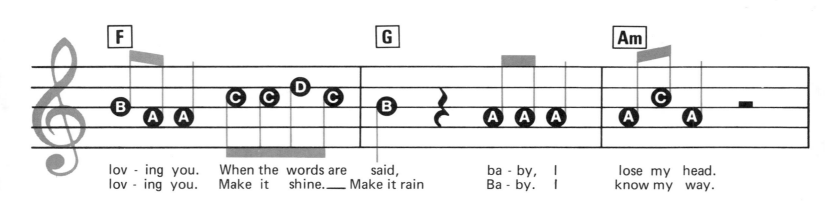

lov-ing you. When the words are said, ba-by, I lose my head.
lov-ing you. Make it shine.___ Make it rain Ba-by. I know my way.

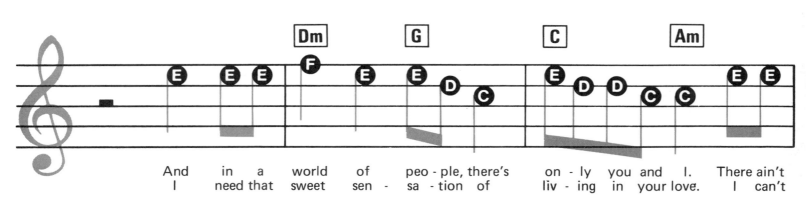

And in a world of peo-ple, there's on-ly you and I. There ain't
I need that sweet sen-sa-tion of liv-ing in your love. I can't

Harper Valley P.T.A.

Registration: *BIG 'N BOLD*

Words and Music by
Tom T. Hall

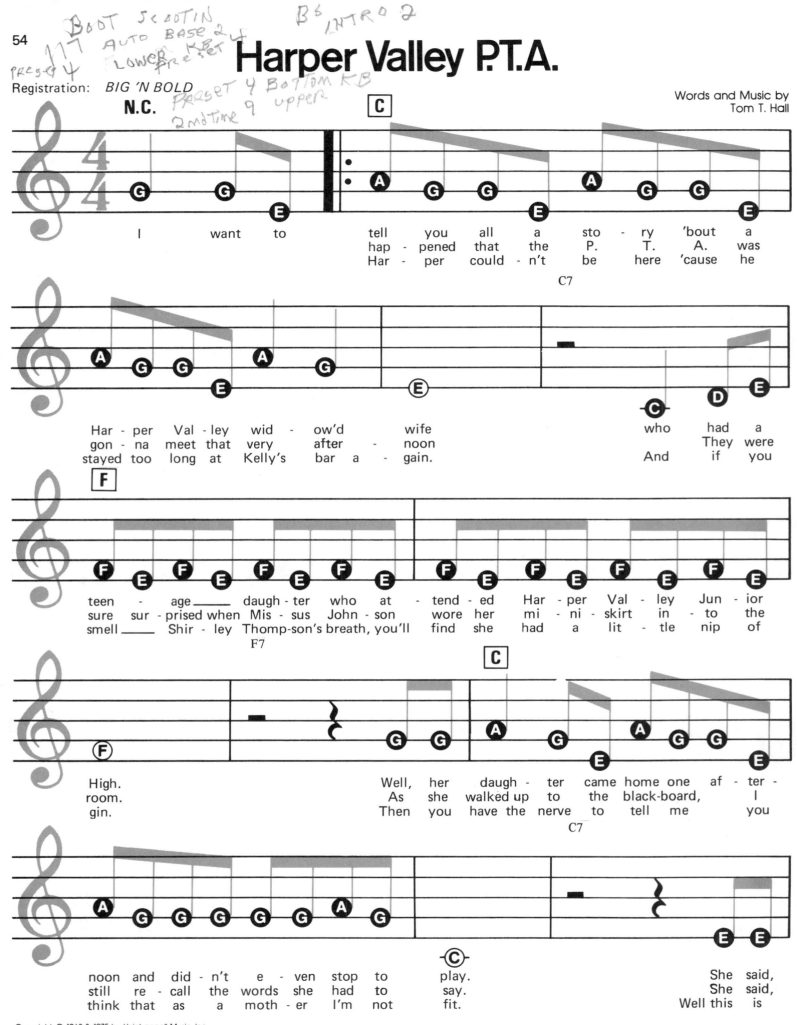

55

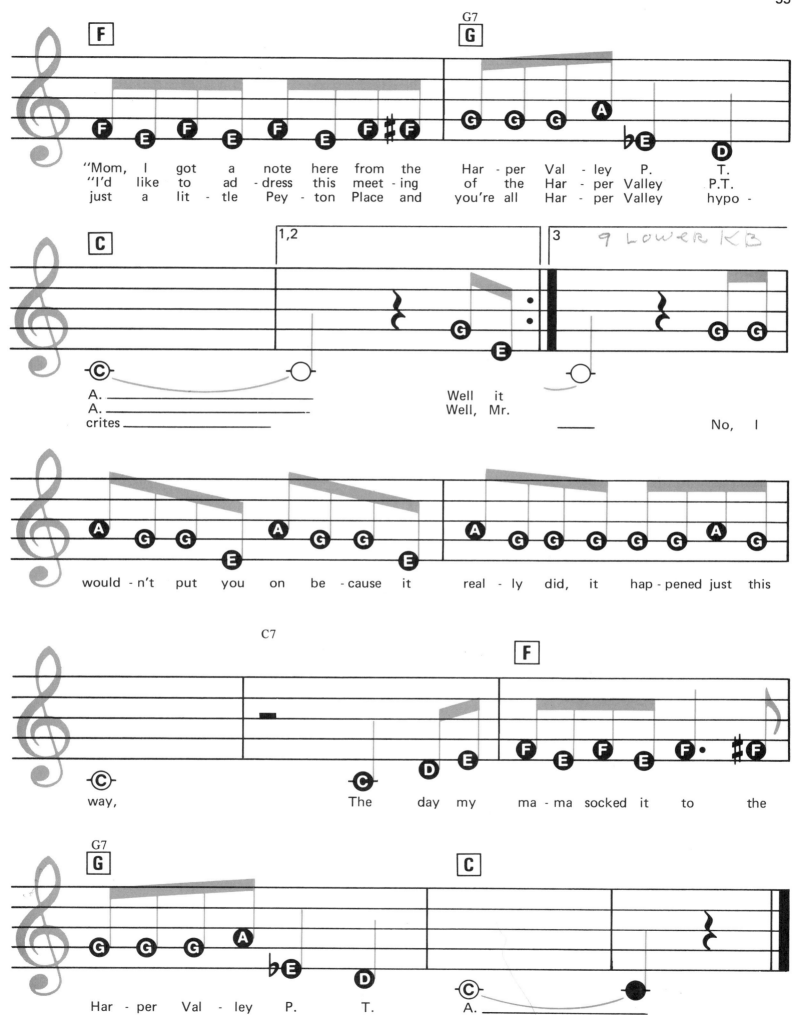

Liebestraum

Registration: *FULL 'N MELLOW*

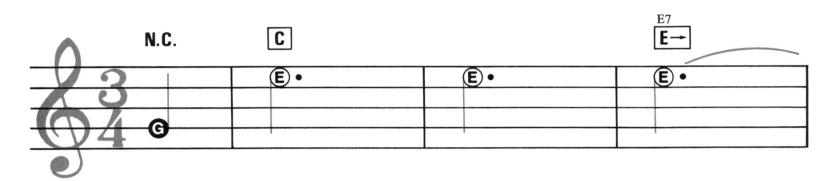

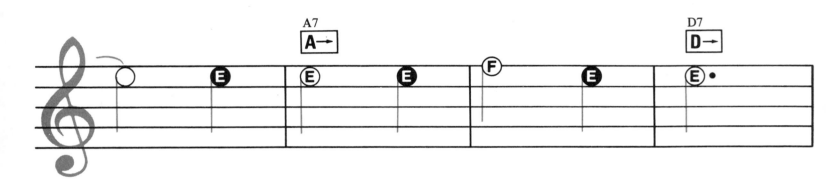

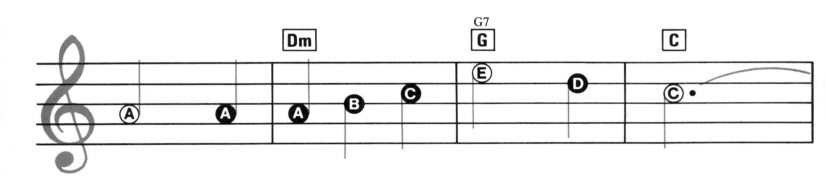

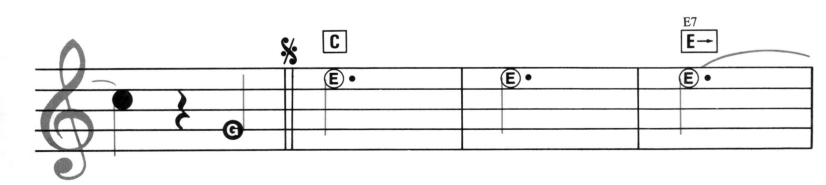

57

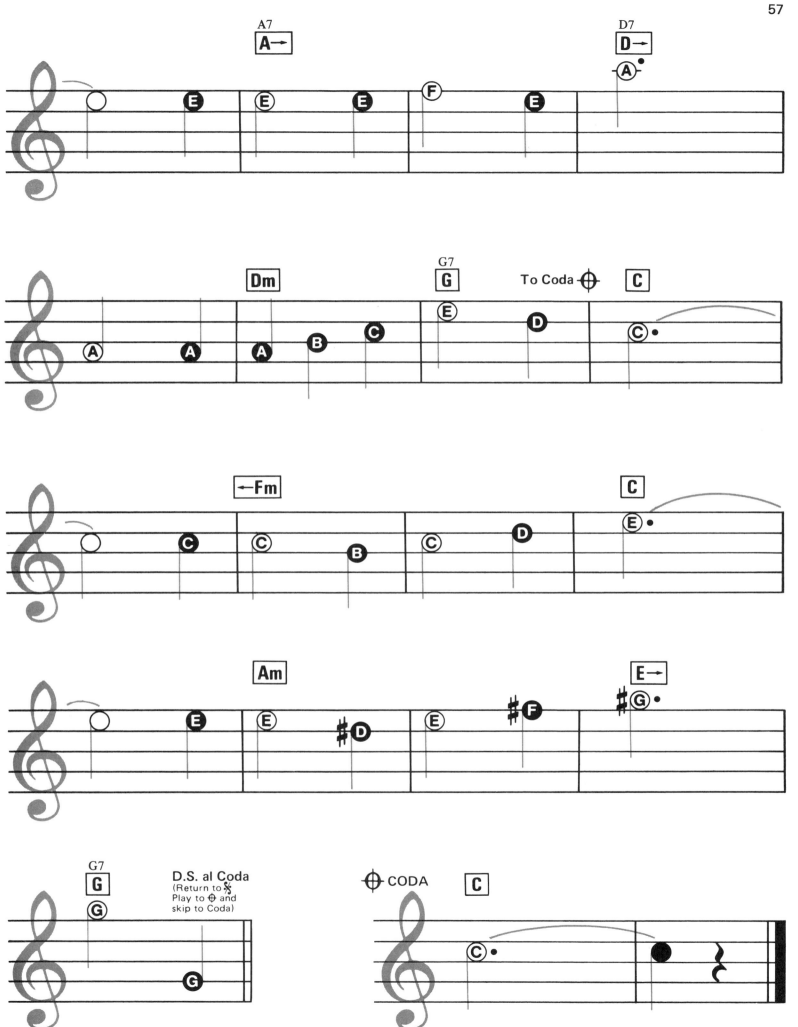

He's Got The Whole World In His Hands

Registration: *FULL 'N' MELLOW*

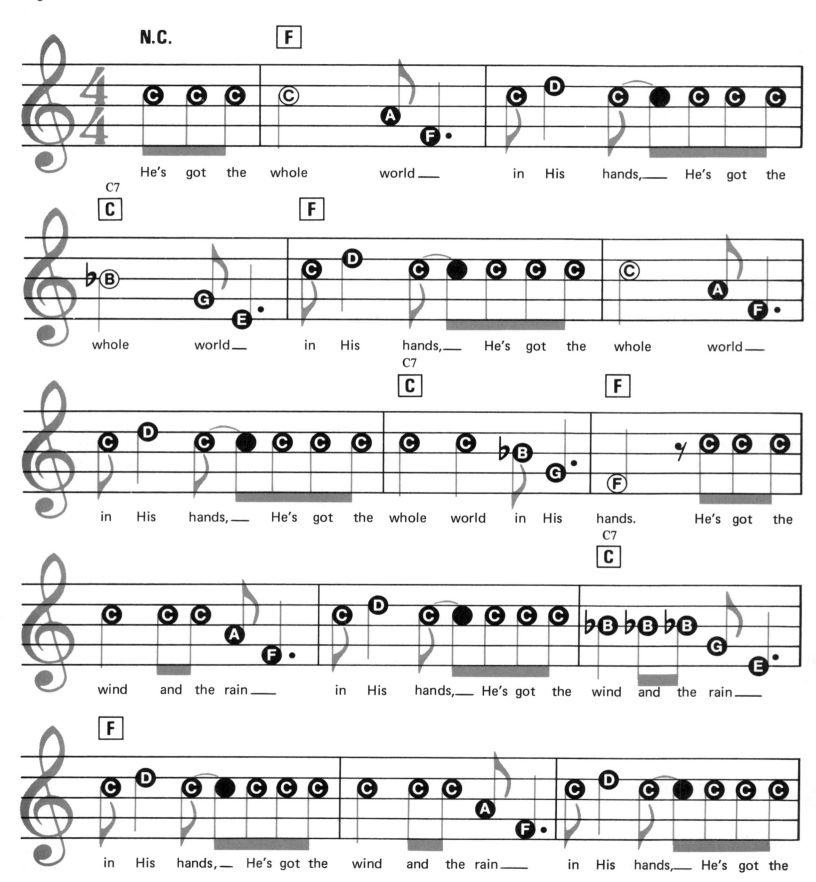

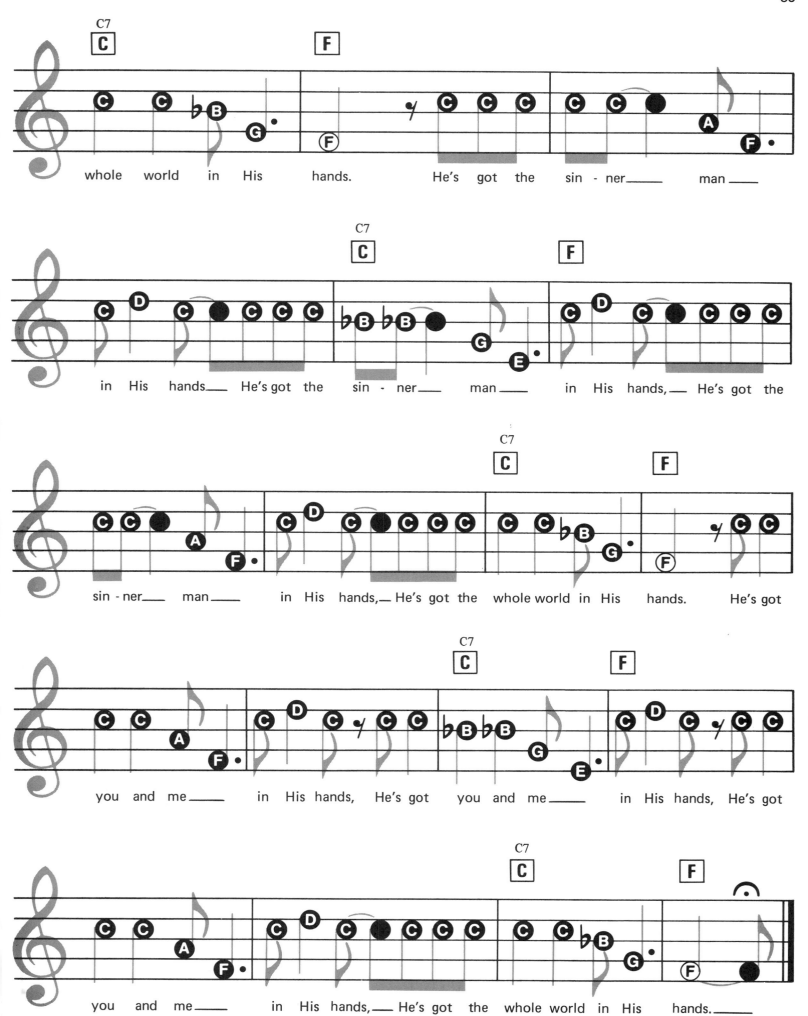

Woodchoppers' Ball

Registration: *BIG 'N BOLD*

By Woody Herman
and Joe Bishop

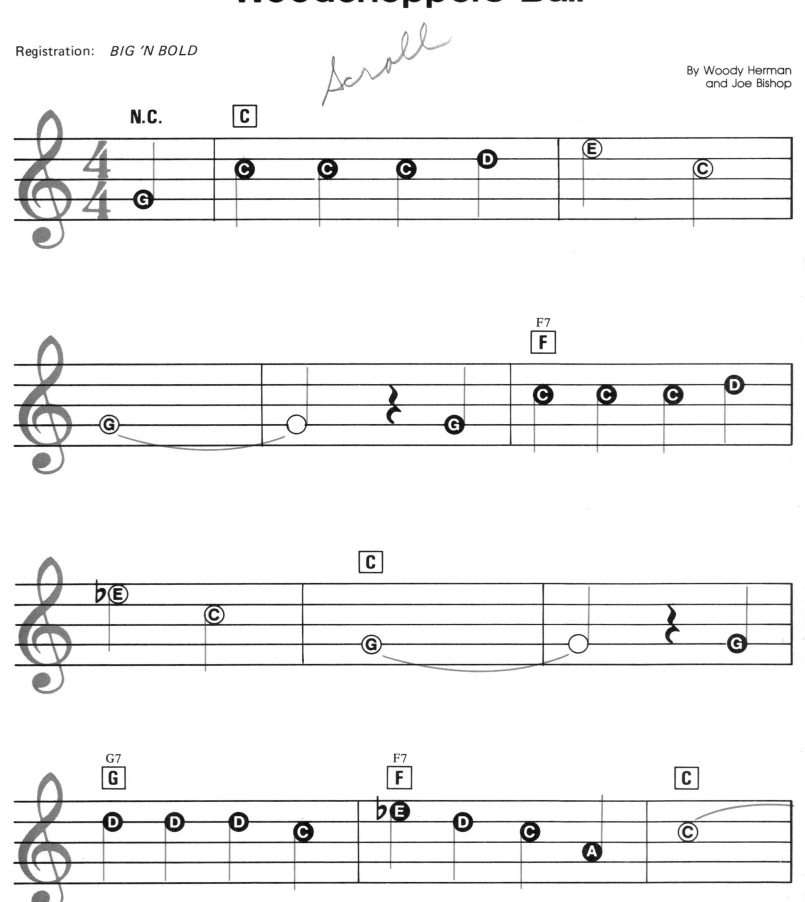

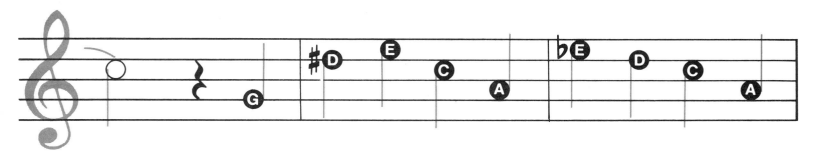
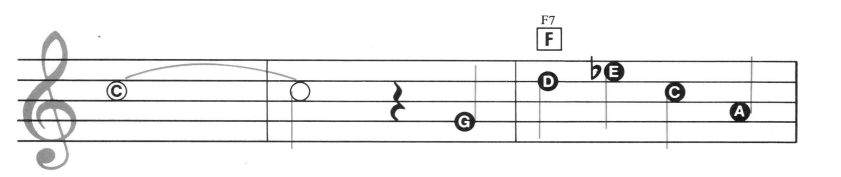
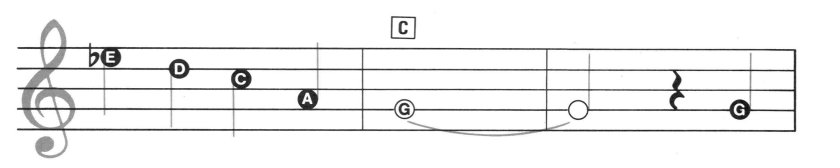
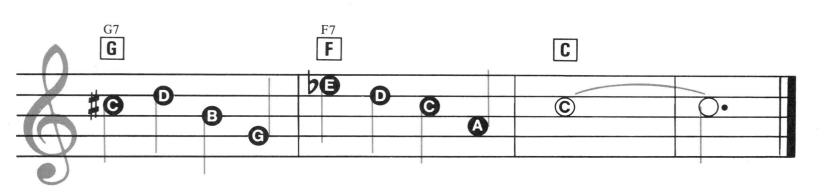

Love Letters In The Sand

Registration: *FULL 'N MELLOW*

By Nick Kenny, Charles Kenny
and J. Fred Coots

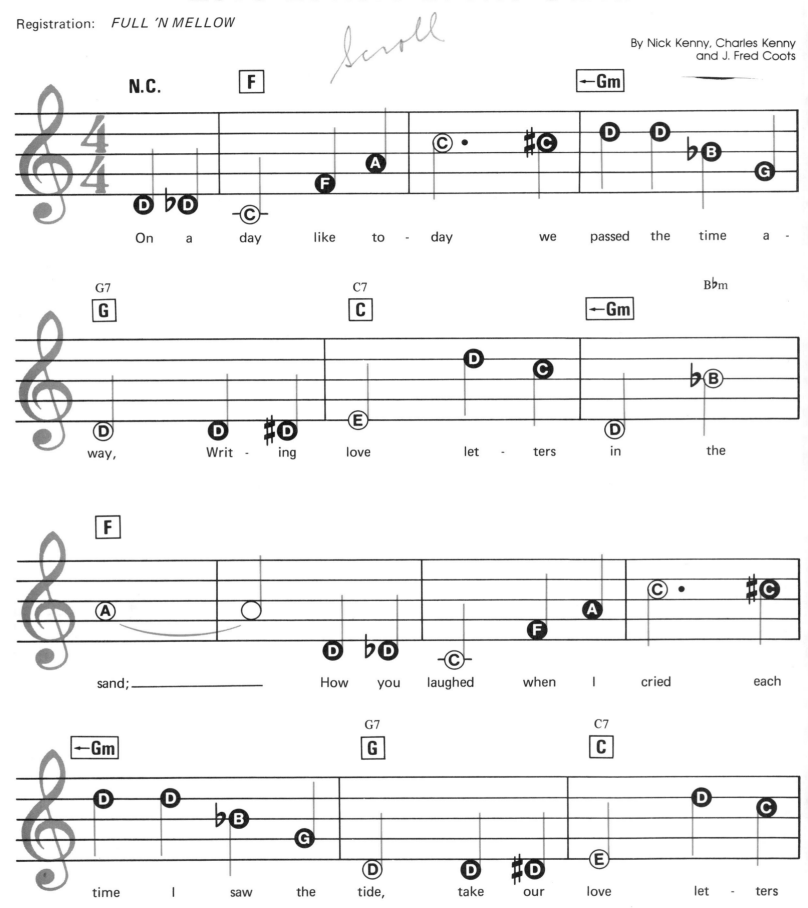

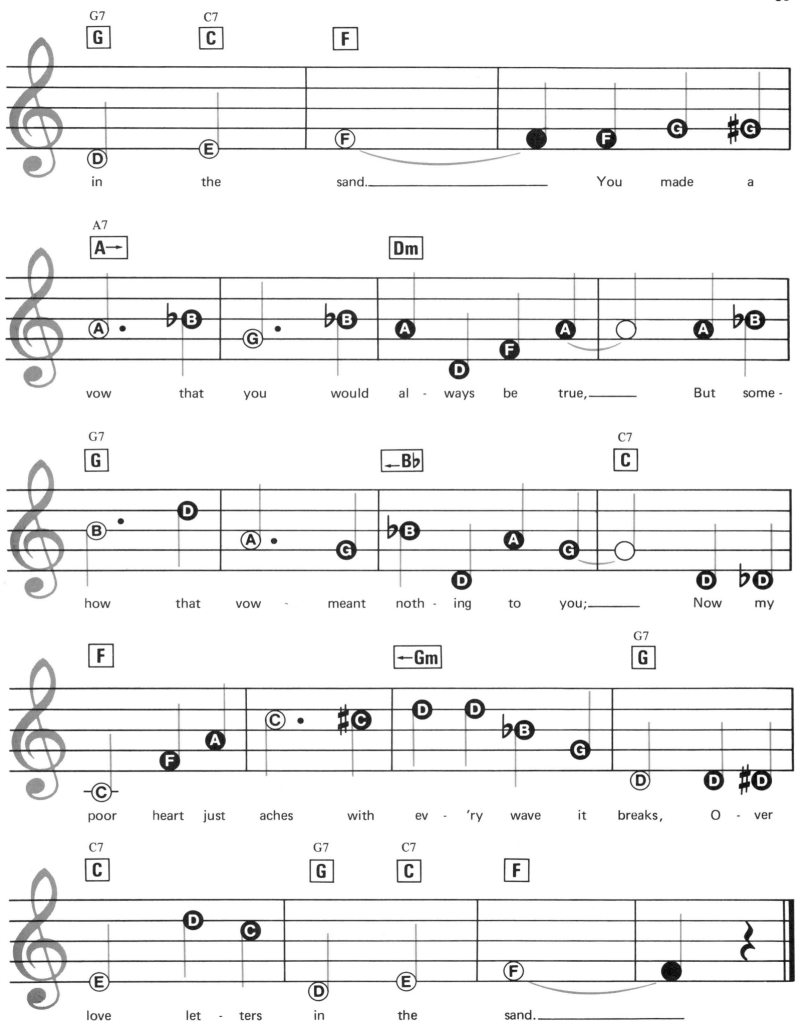

Five Foot Two, Eyes Of Blue

(Has Anybody Seen My Girl?)

Registration: *BRIGHT 'N' BRASSY*

Words by Sam Lewis and Joe Young
Music by Ray Henderson

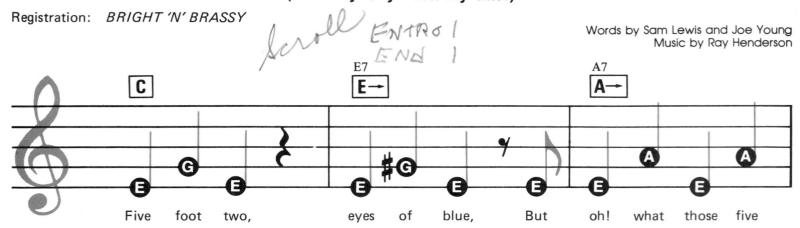

Five foot two, eyes of blue, But oh! what those five

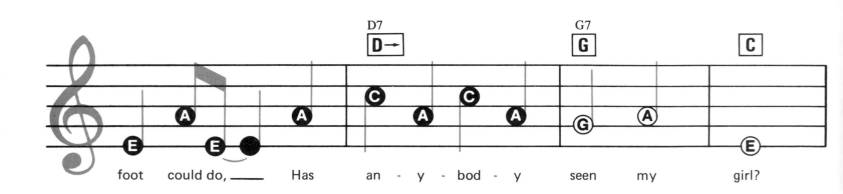

foot could do, ____ Has an - y - bod - y seen my girl?

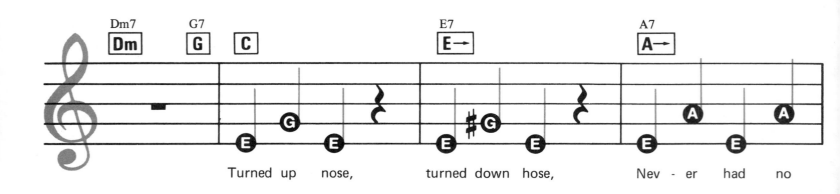

Turned up nose, turned down hose, Nev - er had no

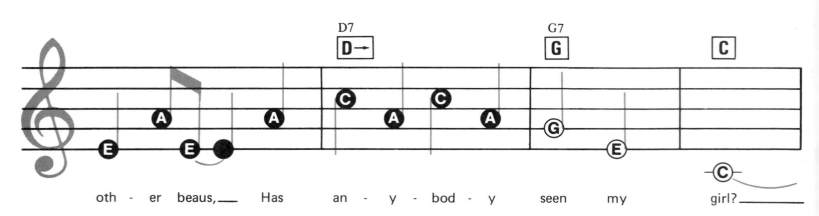

oth - er beaus, ____ Has an - y - bod - y seen my girl? _____

Hello, Dolly!
(From "Hello, Dolly!")

Registration: *FULL 'N BRILLIANT*

Music and Lyric by
Jerry Herman

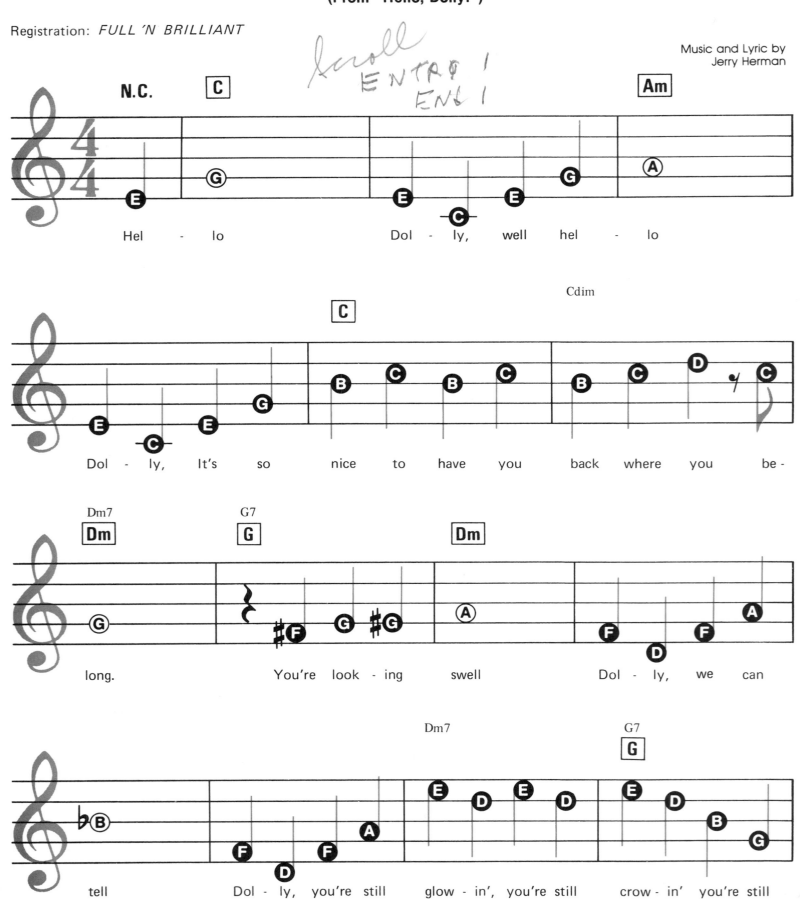

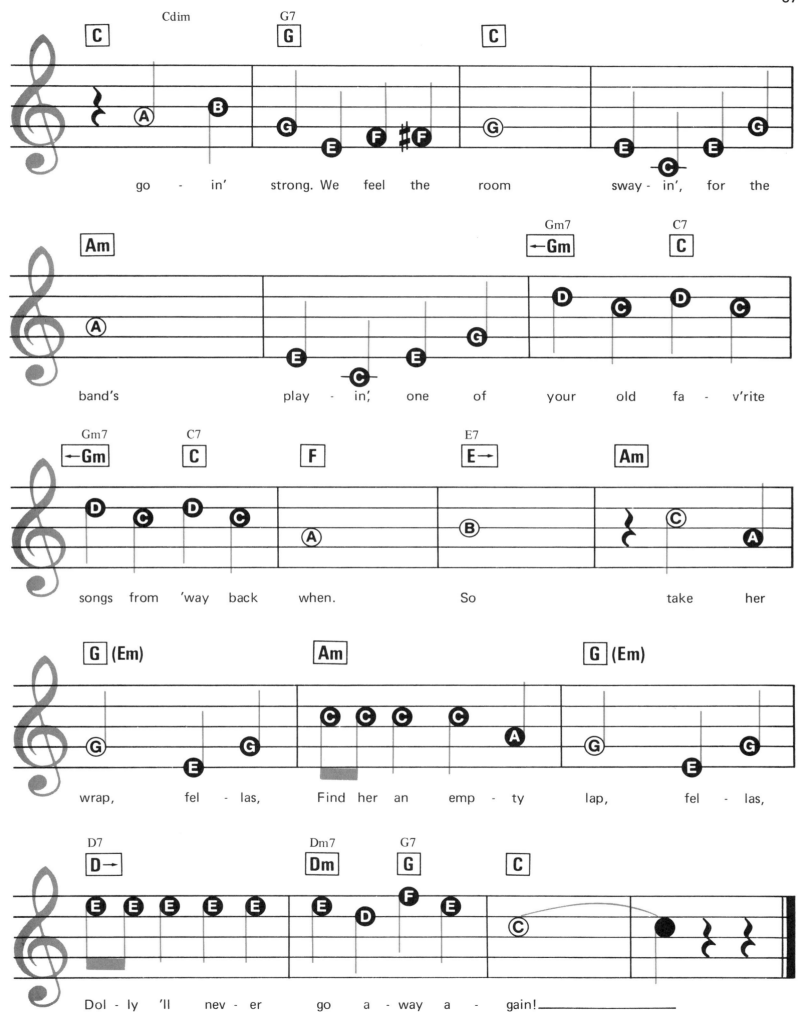

Make The World Go Away

Registration: *SOFT SOLO*
or BALLAD

Words and Music by
Hank Cochran

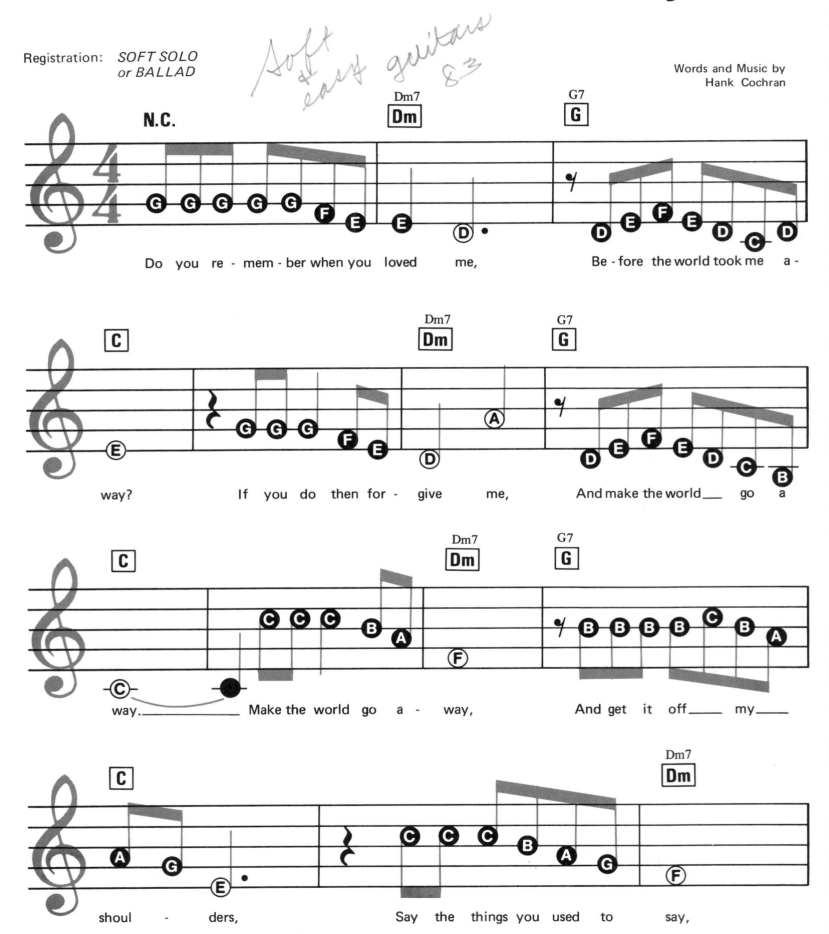

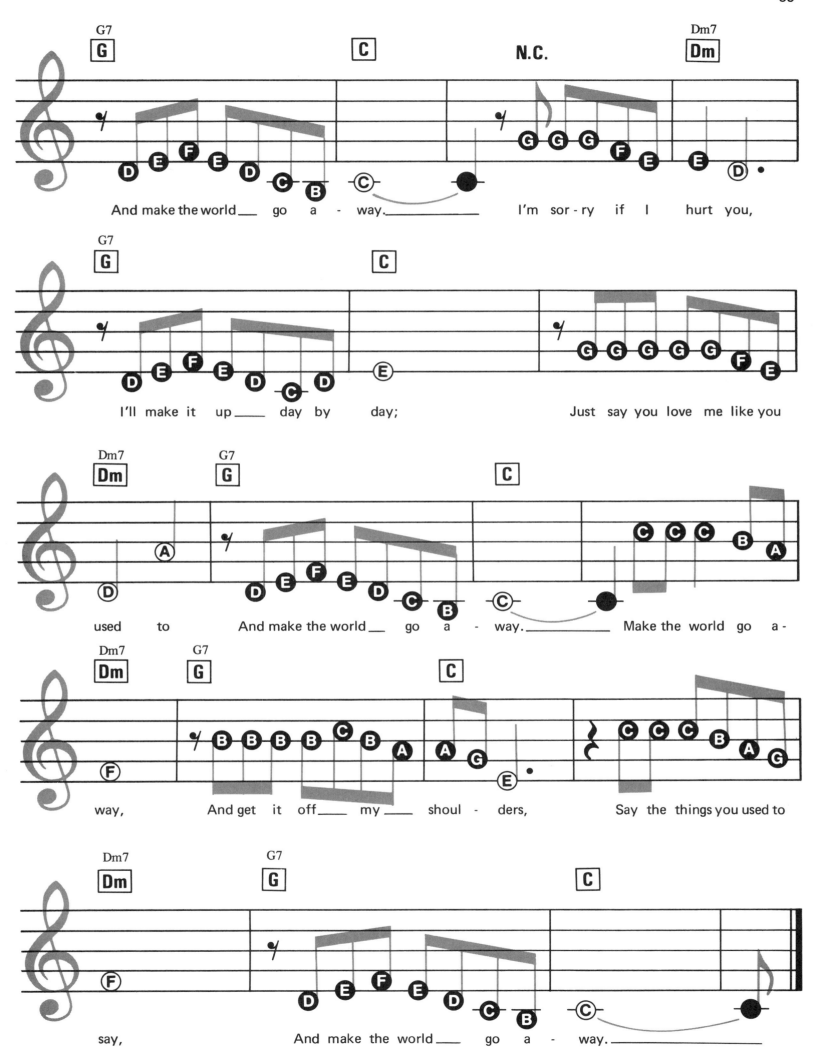

Bluesette

Registration: *BRIGHT 'N BRASSY*

Words by Norman Gimbel
Music by Jean Thielemans

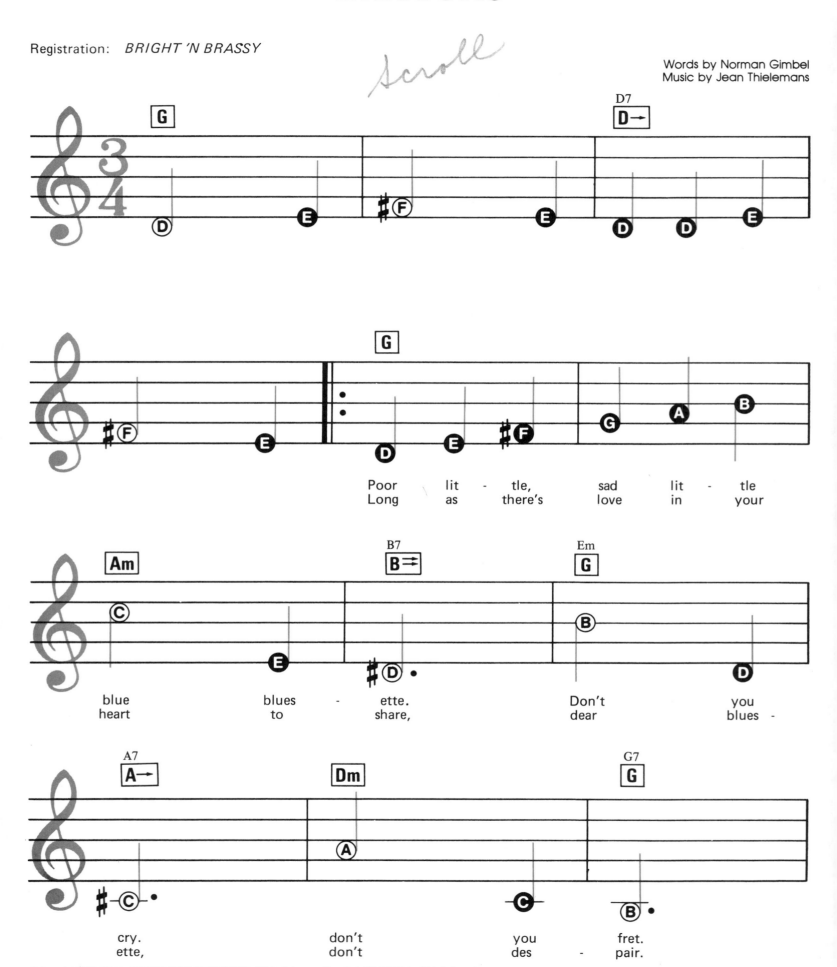

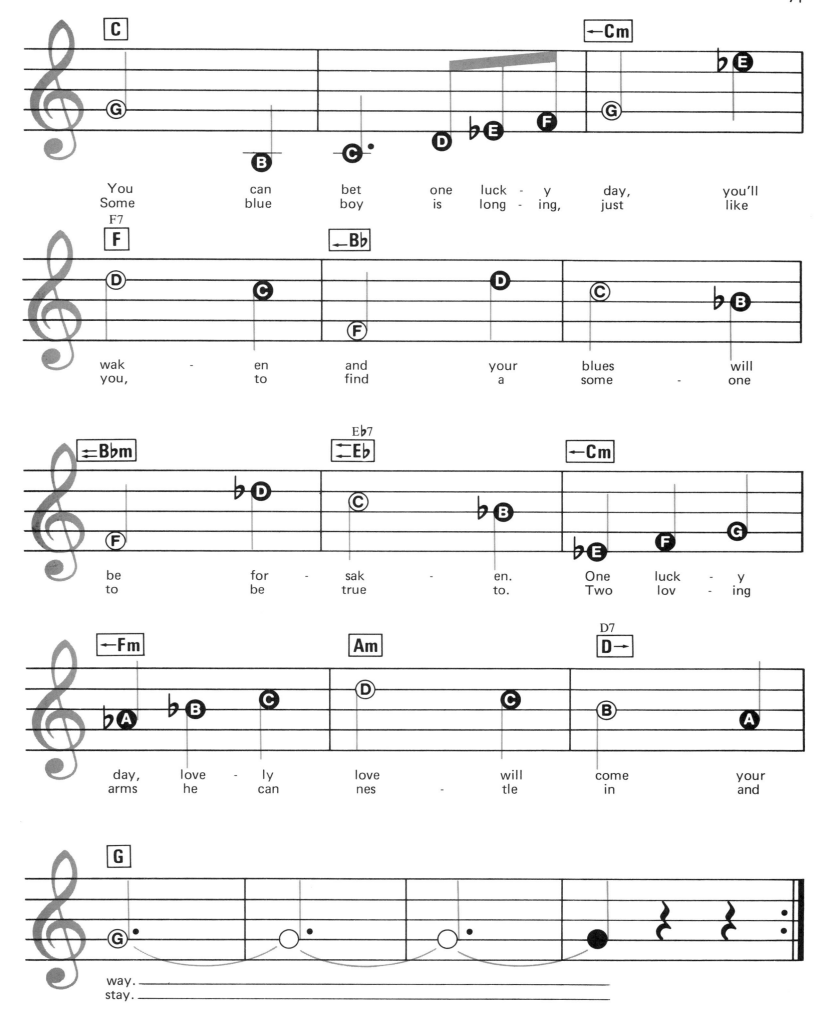

71

(Hey, Won't You Play)

Another Somebody
Done Somebody Wrong Song

Registration: *BIG 'N BOLD*

Words and Music by Larry Butler
and Chips Moman

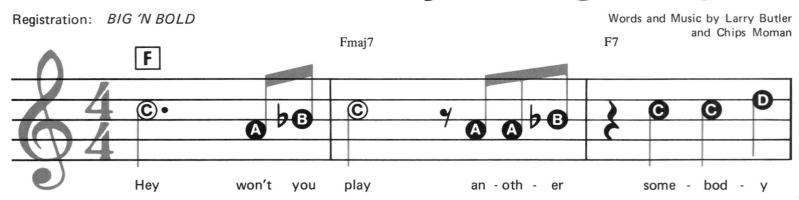

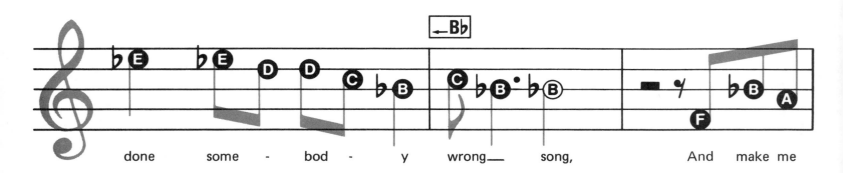

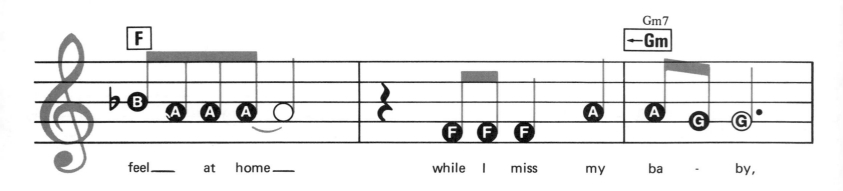

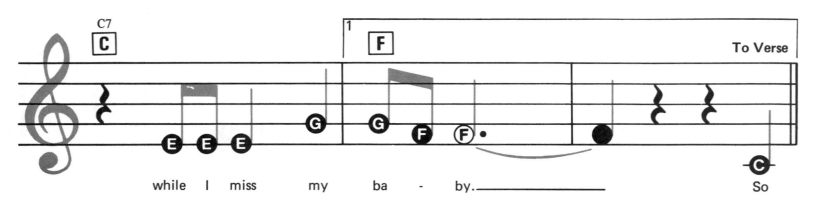

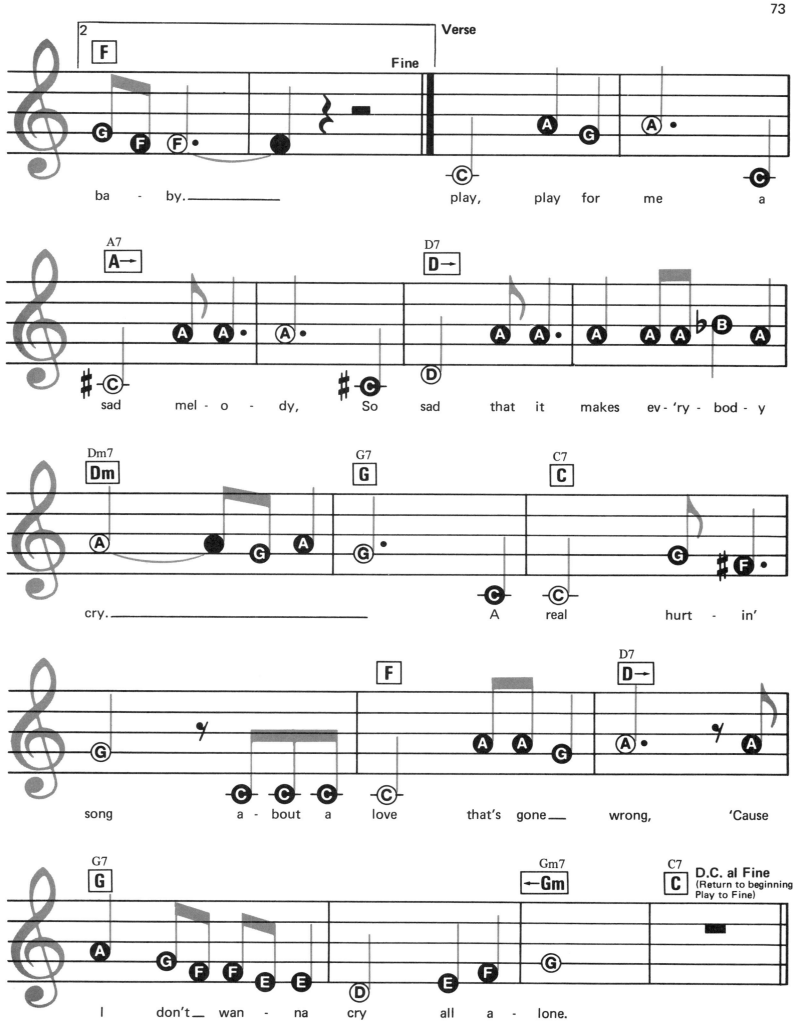

Hernando's Hideaway

Registration: *BRILLIANT SOLO*

Words and Music by
Richard Alder and Jerry Ross

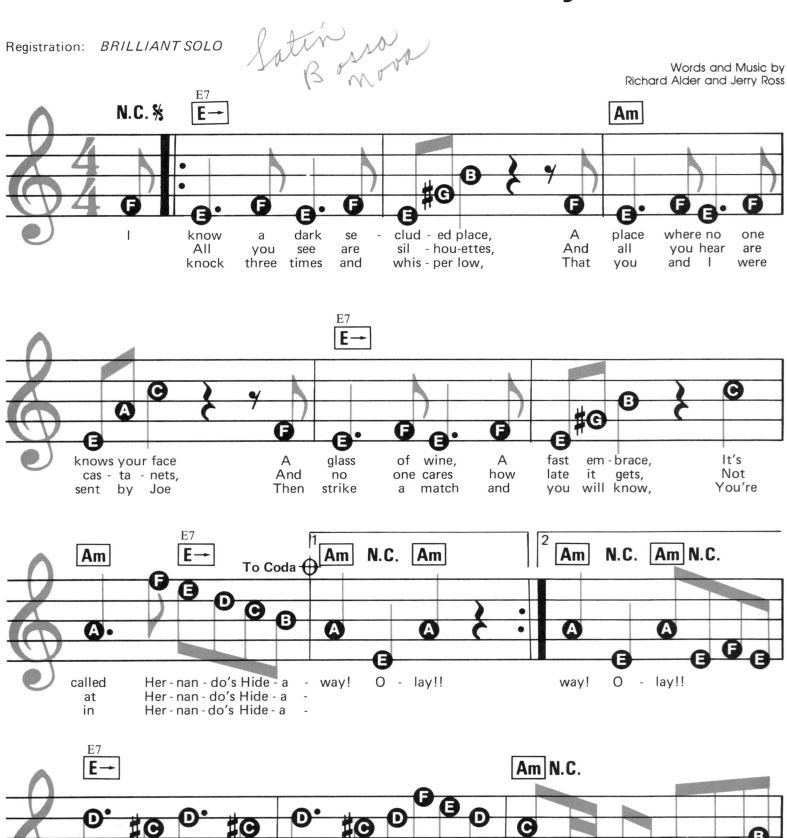

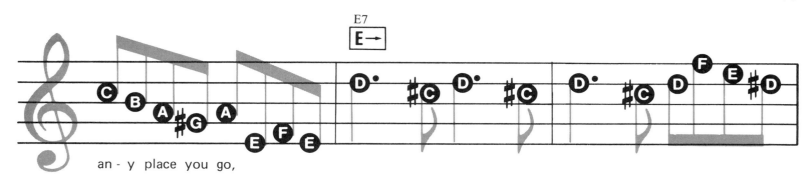

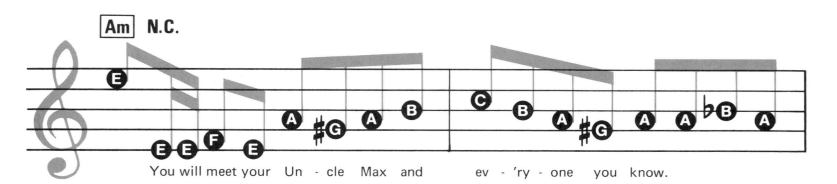

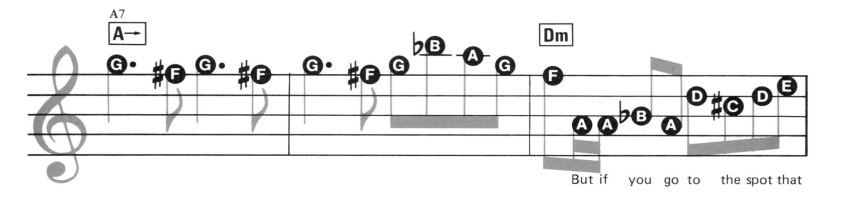

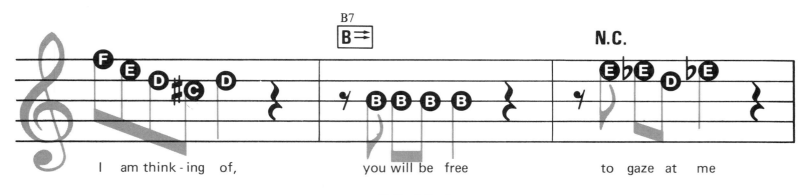

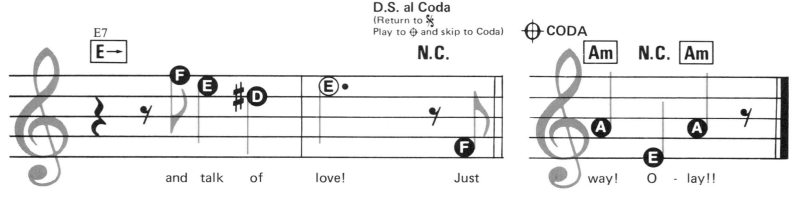

Brazil

Registration: *FULL 'N BRILLIANT*

STICK
Bb 125 ENTRO-1-ENDING-2

English Words by S.K. Russell
Brazilian Samba by Ary Barroso

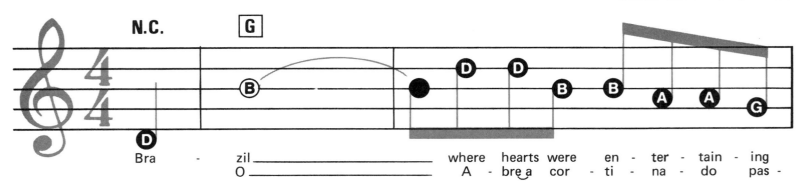

Bra - zil _____ where hearts were en - ter - tain - ing
O _____ A - bre a cor - ti - na - do pas -

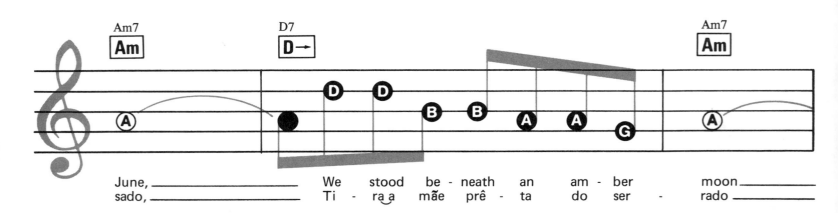

June, _____ We stood be - neath an am - ber moon _____
sado, _____ Ti - ra a mãe prê - ta do ser - rado _____

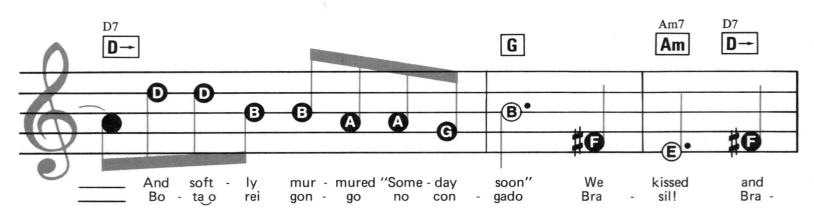

_____ And soft - ly mur - mured "Some - day soon" We kissed and
_____ Bo - ta o rei gon - go no con - gado Bra - sil! Bra -

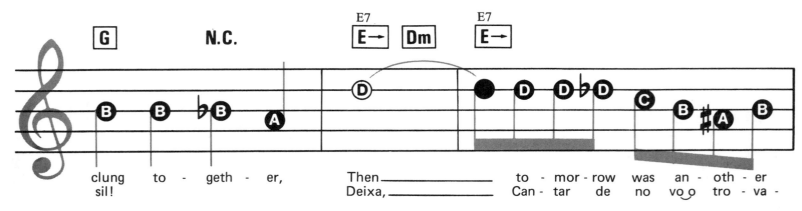

clung to - geth - er, Then _____ to - mor - row was an - oth - er
sil! Deixa, _____ Can - tar de no vo o tro - va -

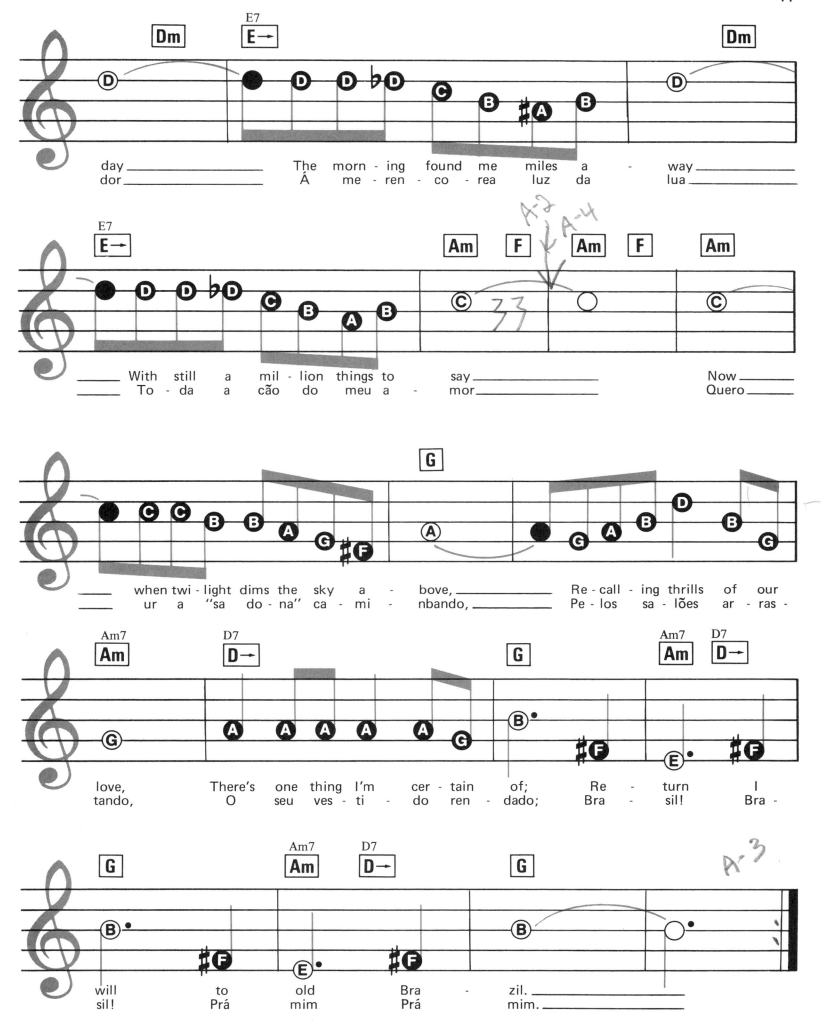

Our Day Will Come

Registration: *BIG 'N BOLD*

Words by Bob Hilliard
Music by Mort Garson

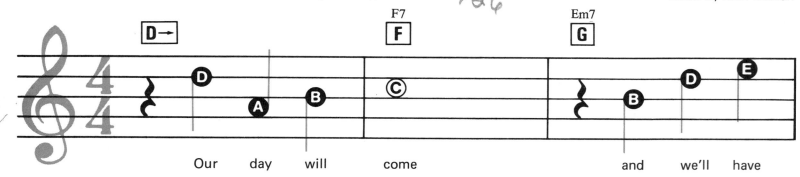

Our day will come and we'll have

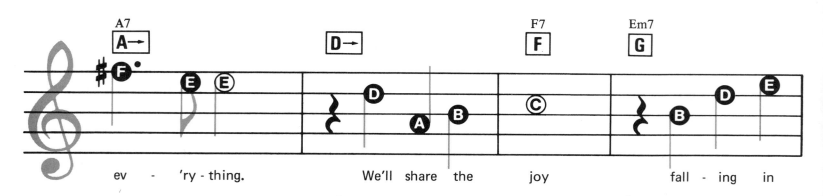

ev - 'ry - thing. We'll share the joy fall - ing in

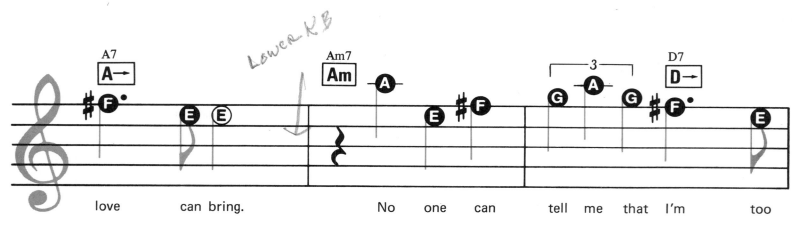

love can bring. No one can tell me that I'm too

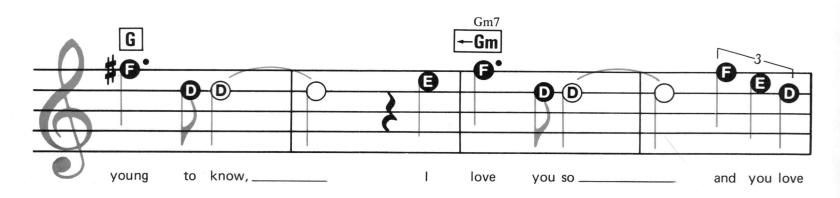

young to know, _____ I love you so _____ and you love

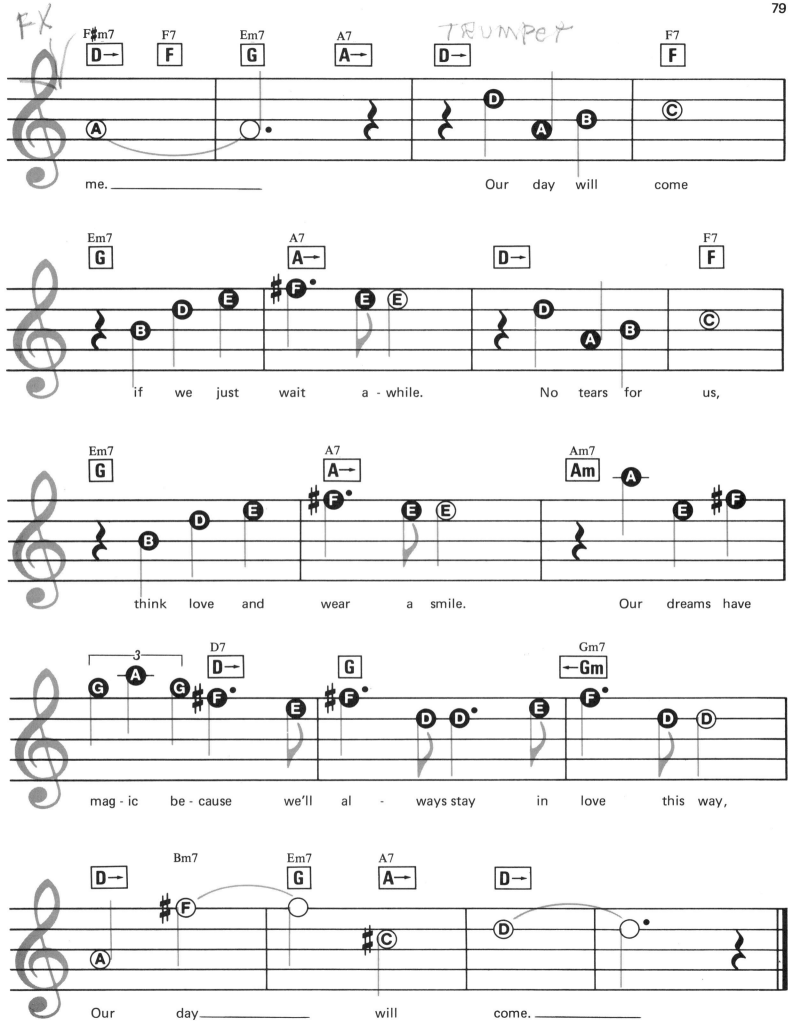

Green Eyes
(Aquellos Ojos Verdes)

Registration: *BRIGHT 'N BRASSY*

Spanish Lyric by Adolfo Utrera
Music by Nilo Menenez
Translation by E. Rivera and E. Woods

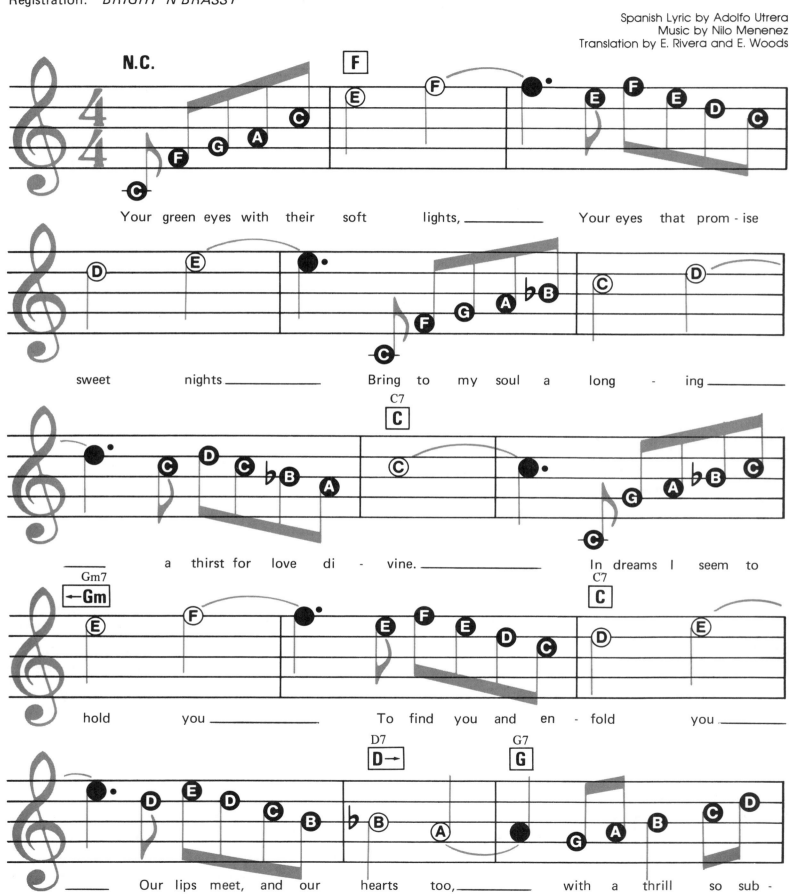

81

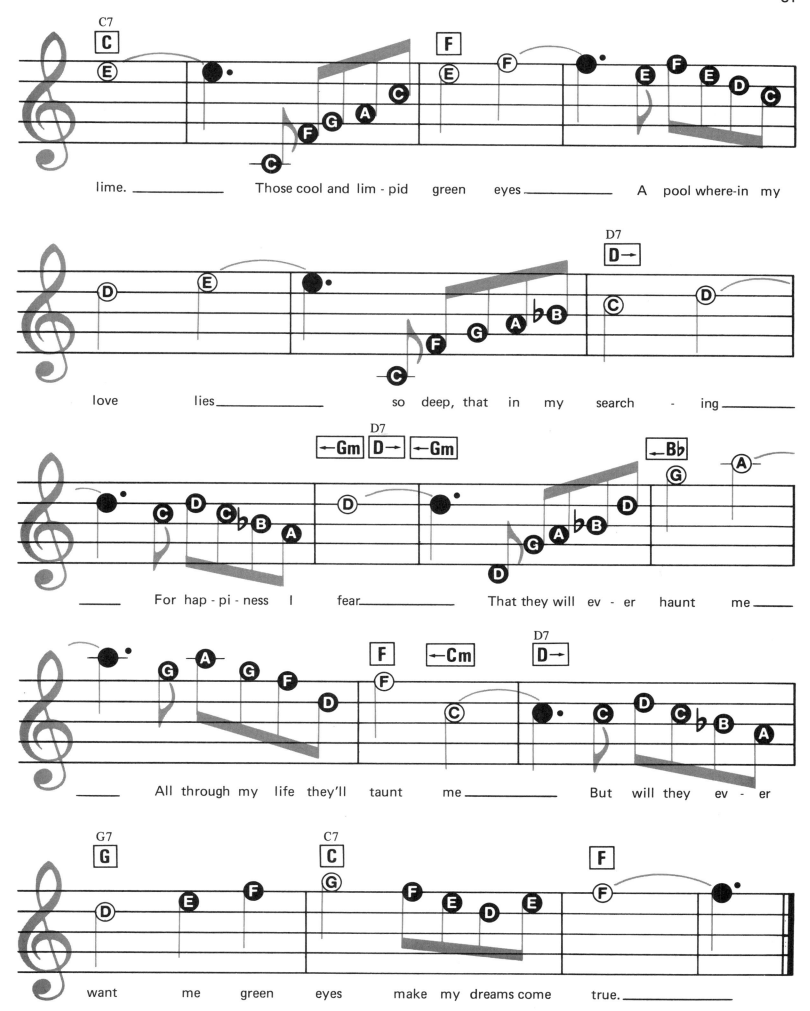

Cherry Pink And Apple Blossom White

Registration: *BIG 'N BOLD*

French Words by Jacques Larus
English Words by Mack David
Music by Louiguy

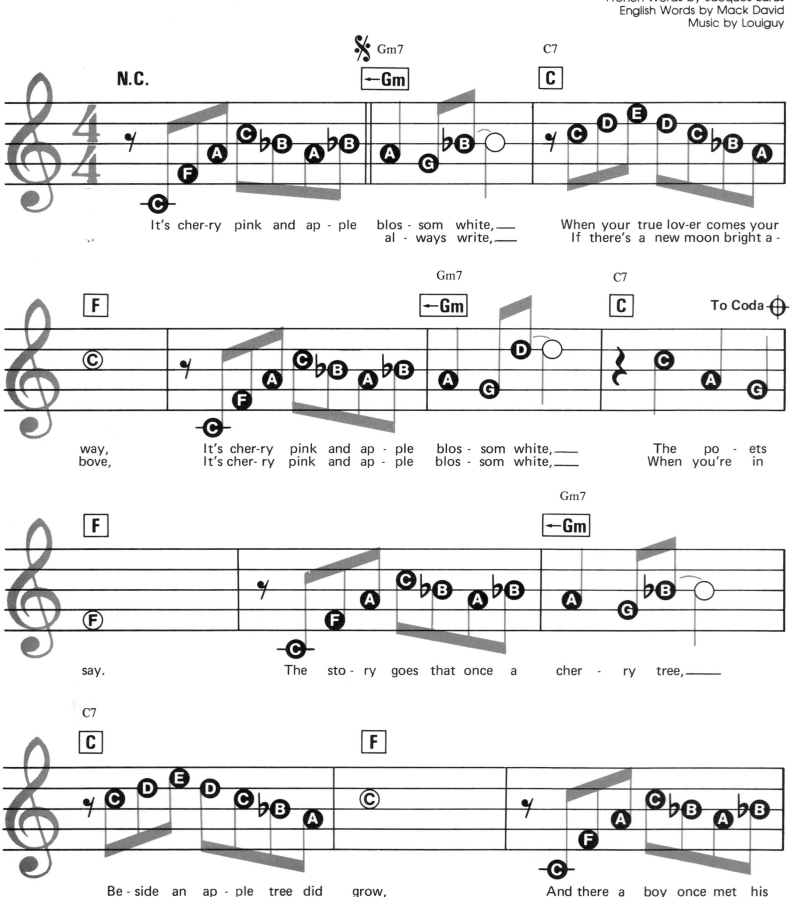

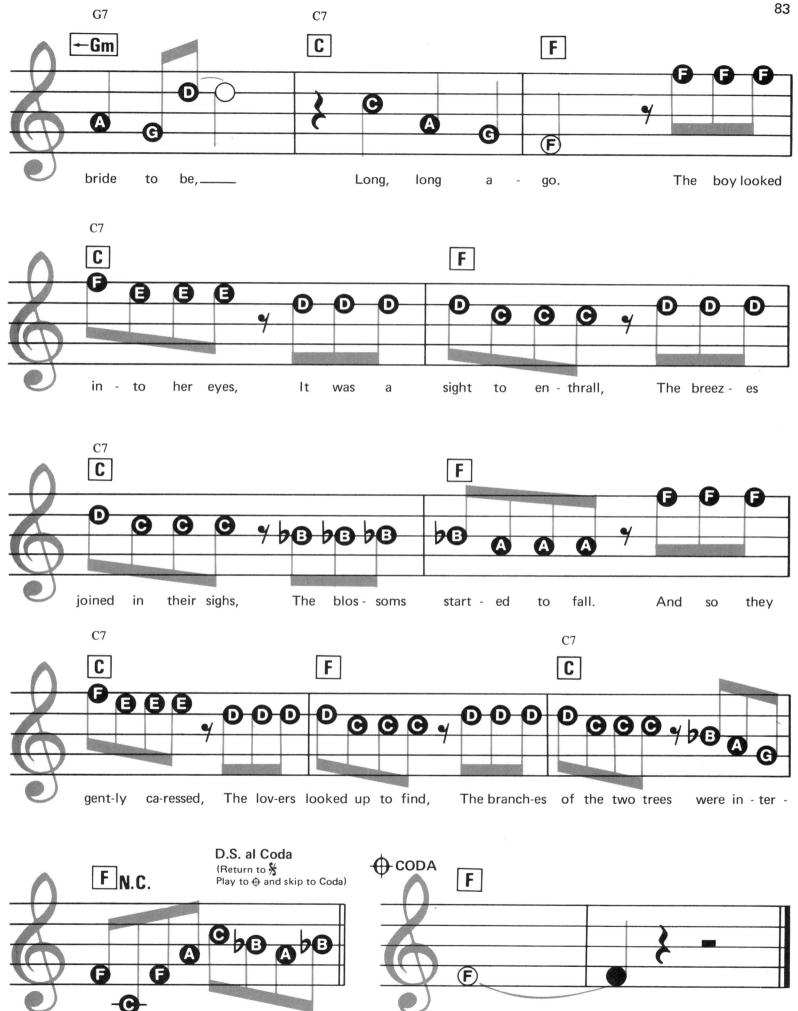

Patricia, It's Patricia

Registration: *BRIGHT 'N BRASSY*

Lyric by Bob Marcus
Music by Perez Prado

85

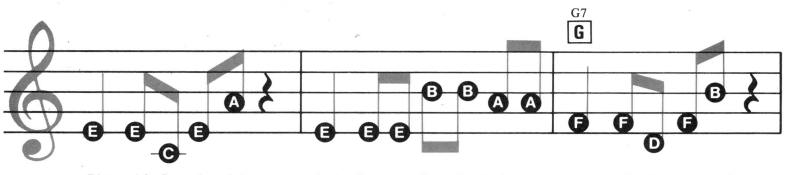

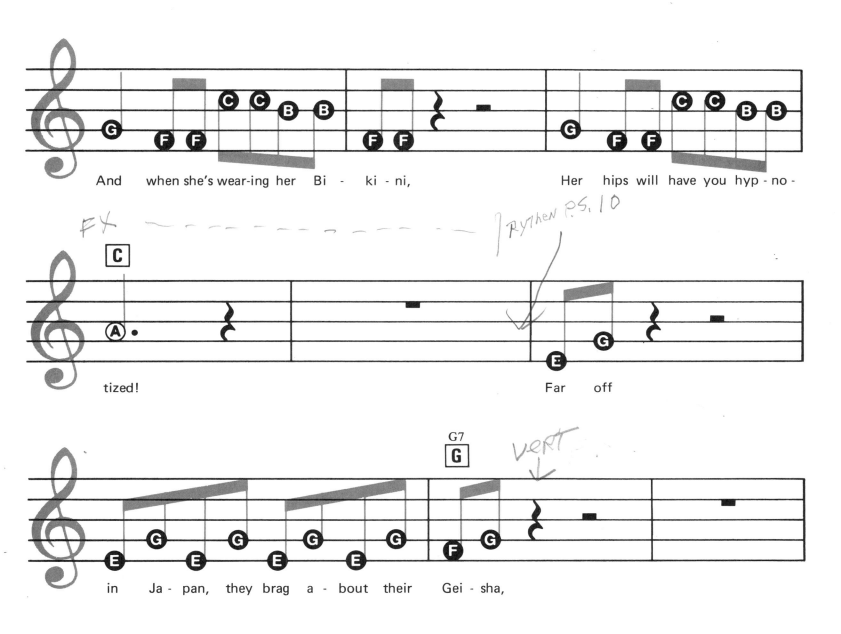

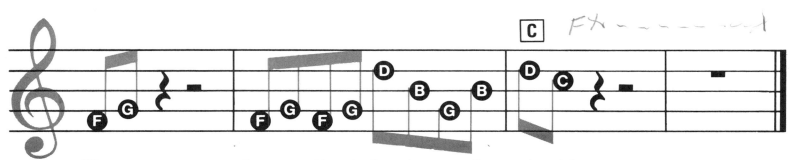

How Can You Mend A Broken Heart

Registration: *BIG 'N BOLD*

Words and Music by
Barry and Robin Gibb

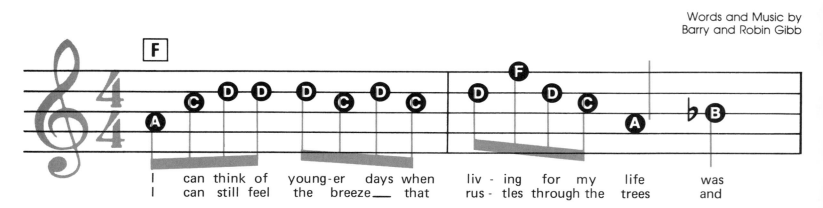

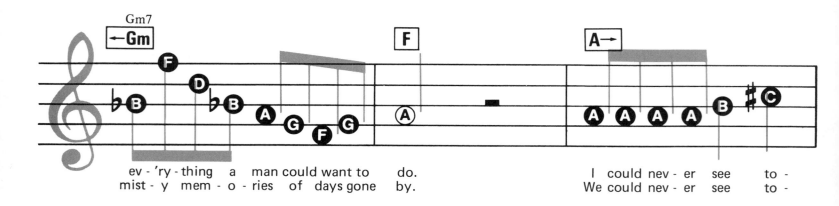

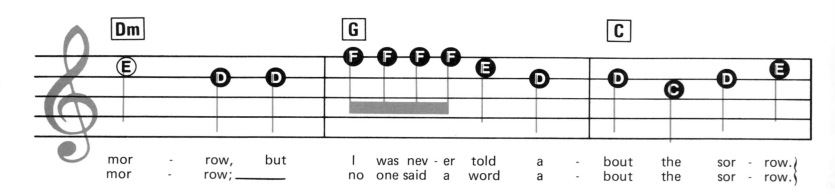

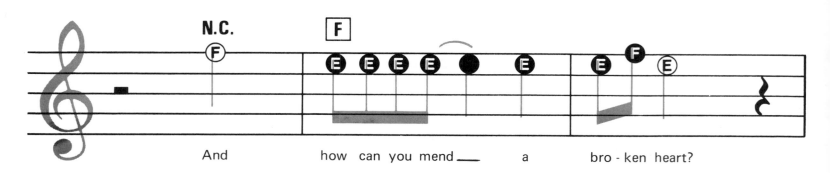

Seventy Six Trombones

Registration: *BRIGHT 'N BRASSY*

Words and Music by
Meredith Willson

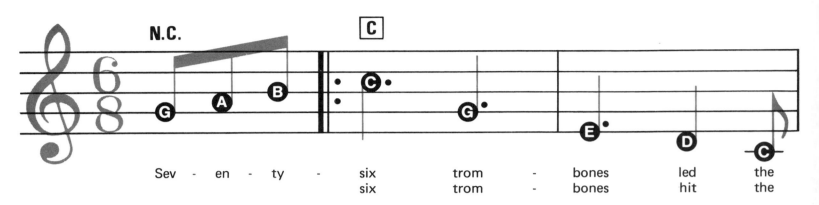

Sev - en - ty - six trom - bones led the
six trom - bones hit the

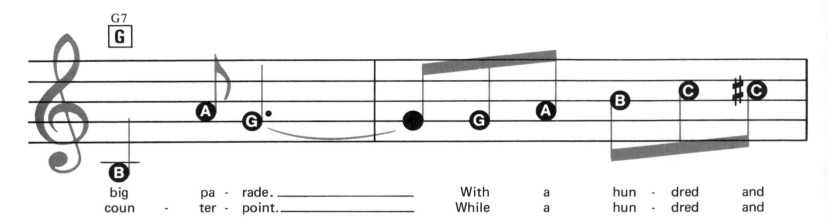

big pa - rade._____ With a hun - dred and
coun - ter - point._____ While a hun - dred and

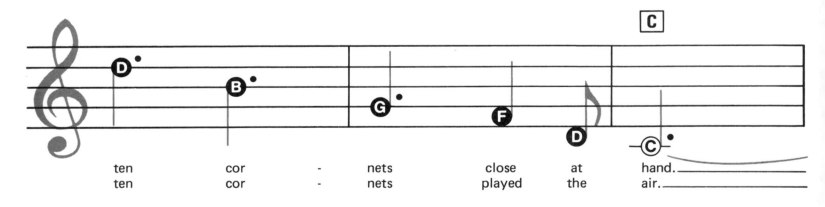

ten cor - nets close at hand._____
ten cor - nets played the air._____

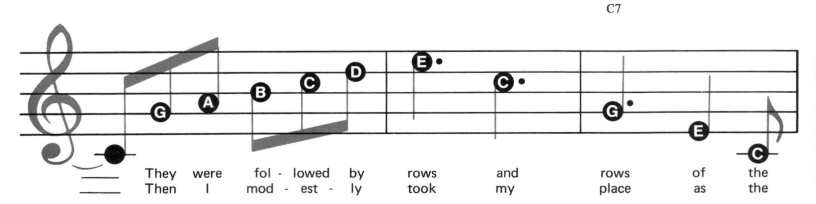

They were fol - lowed by rows and rows of the
Then I mod - est - ly took my place as the

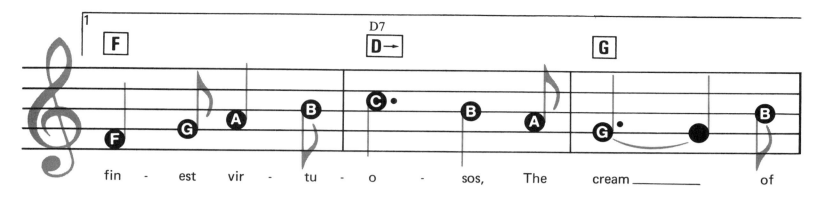

fin - est vir - tu - o - sos, The cream _____ of

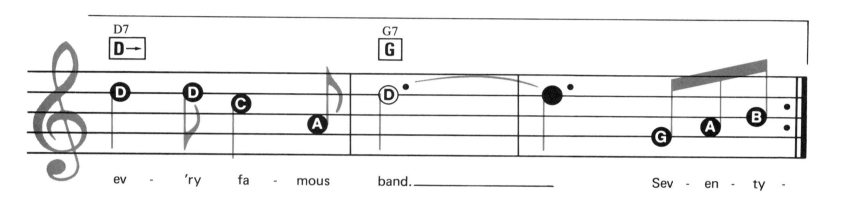

ev - 'ry fa - mous band._____ Sev - en - ty -

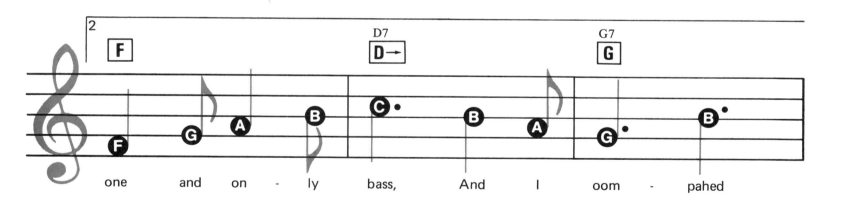

one and on - ly bass, And I oom - pahed

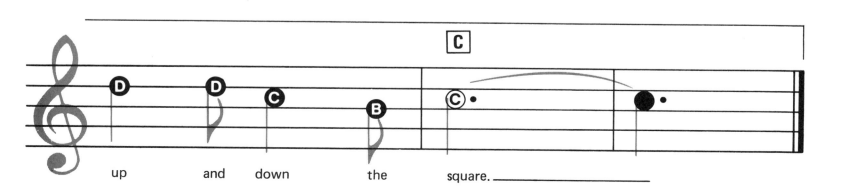

up and down the square._____

Song Sung Blue

Registration: *SOFT SOLO*

Words and Music by
Neil Diamond

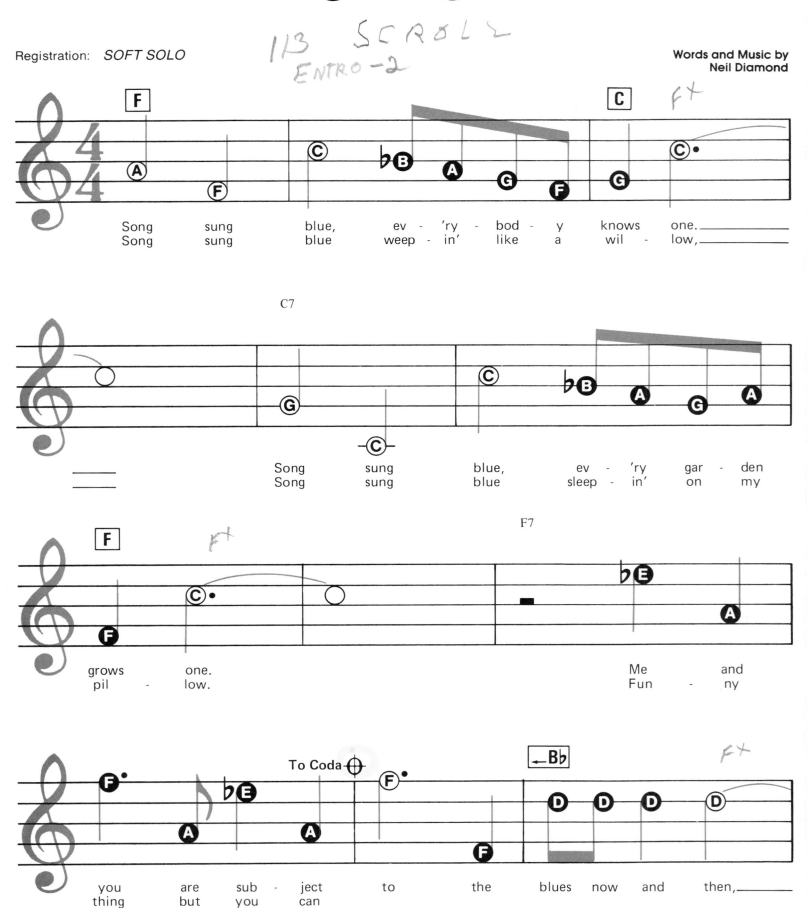

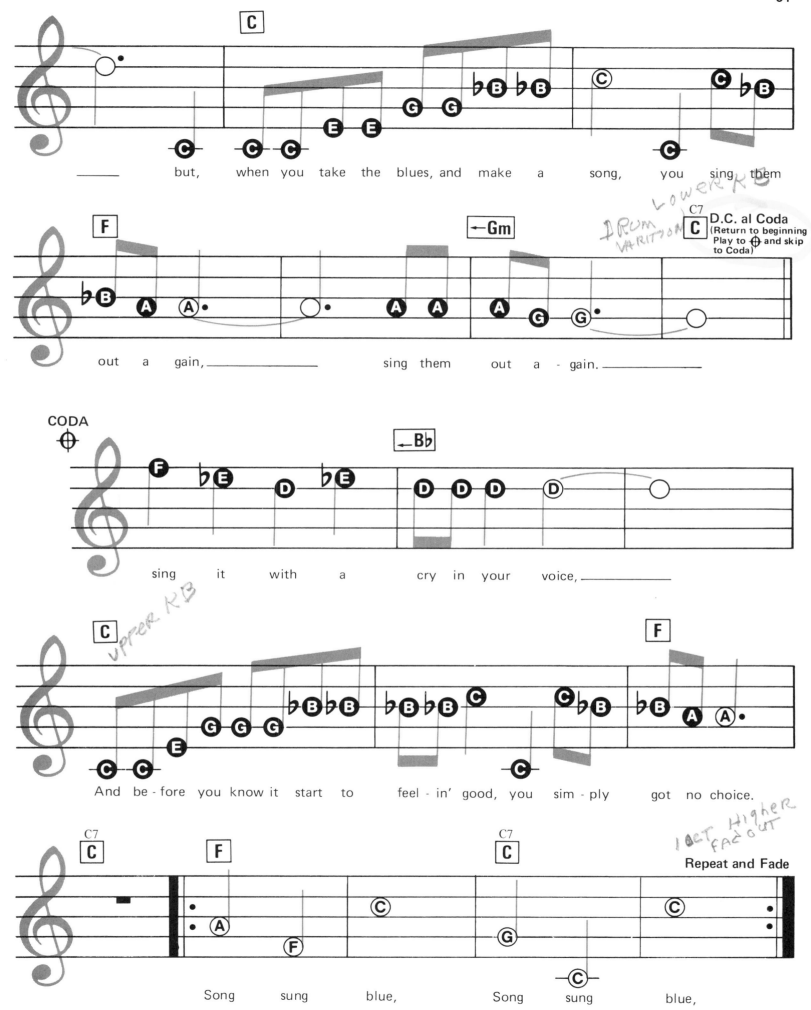

Pennsylvania Polka

Registration: *BRIGHT 'N' BRASSY*

SCROLC

By Lester Lee and Zeke Manners

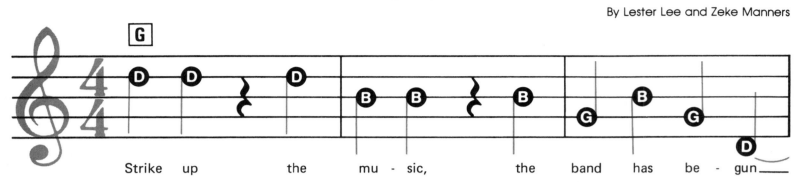

Strike up the mu - sic, the band has be - gun

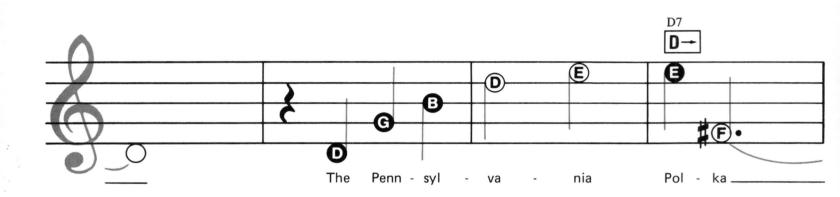

The Penn - syl - va - nia Pol - ka

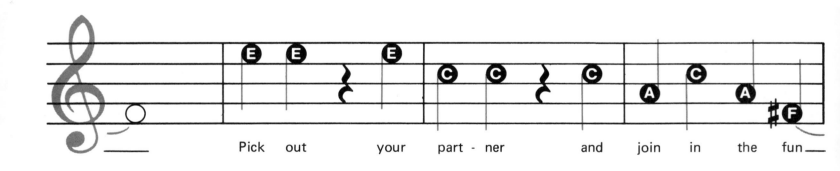

Pick out your part - ner and join in the fun

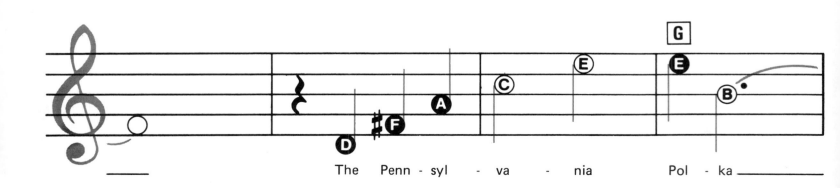

The Penn - syl - va - nia Pol - ka

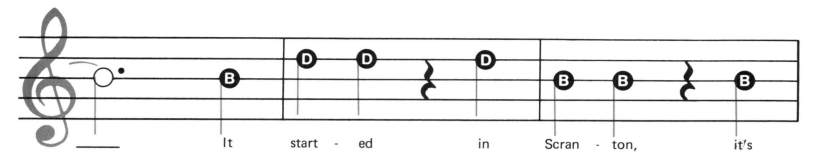

It start - ed in Scran - ton, it's

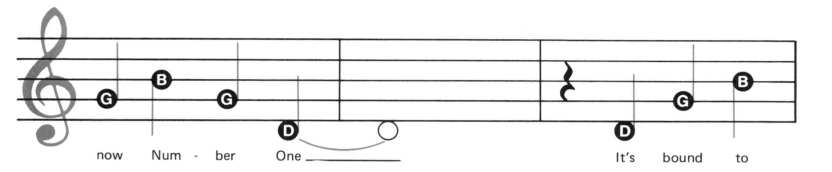

now Num - ber One _____ It's bound to

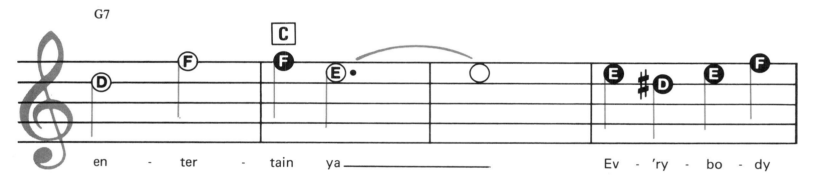

en - ter - tain ya _____ Ev - 'ry - bo - dy

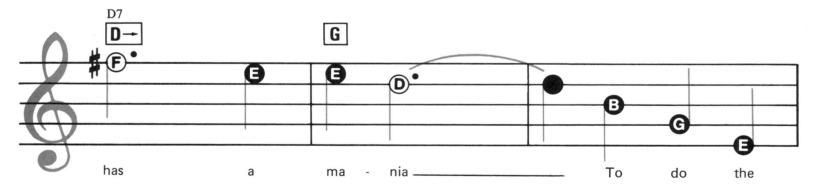

has a ma - nia _____ To do the

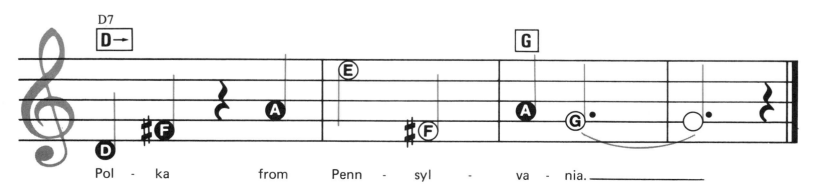

Pol - ka from Penn - syl - va - nia. _____

Grandfather's Clock

Registration: *CLASSICAL*

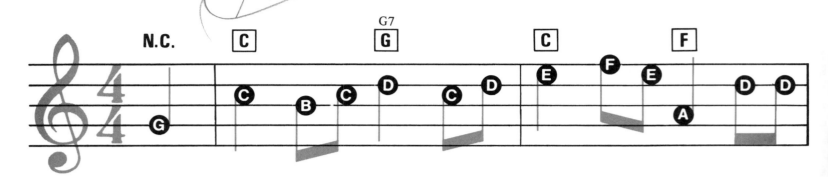

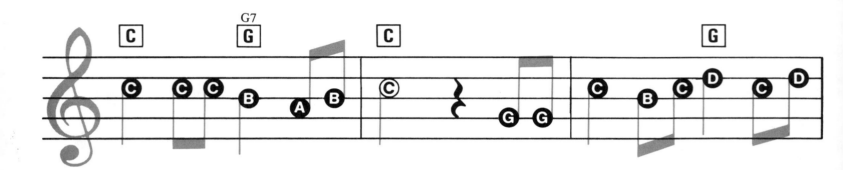

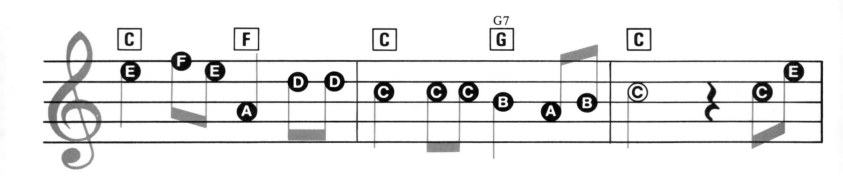

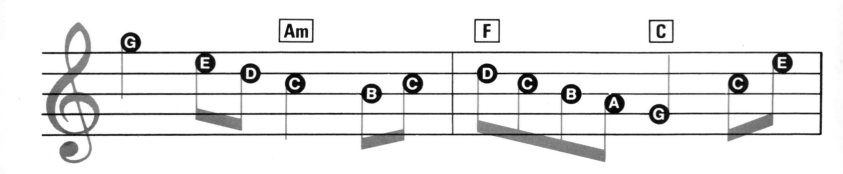

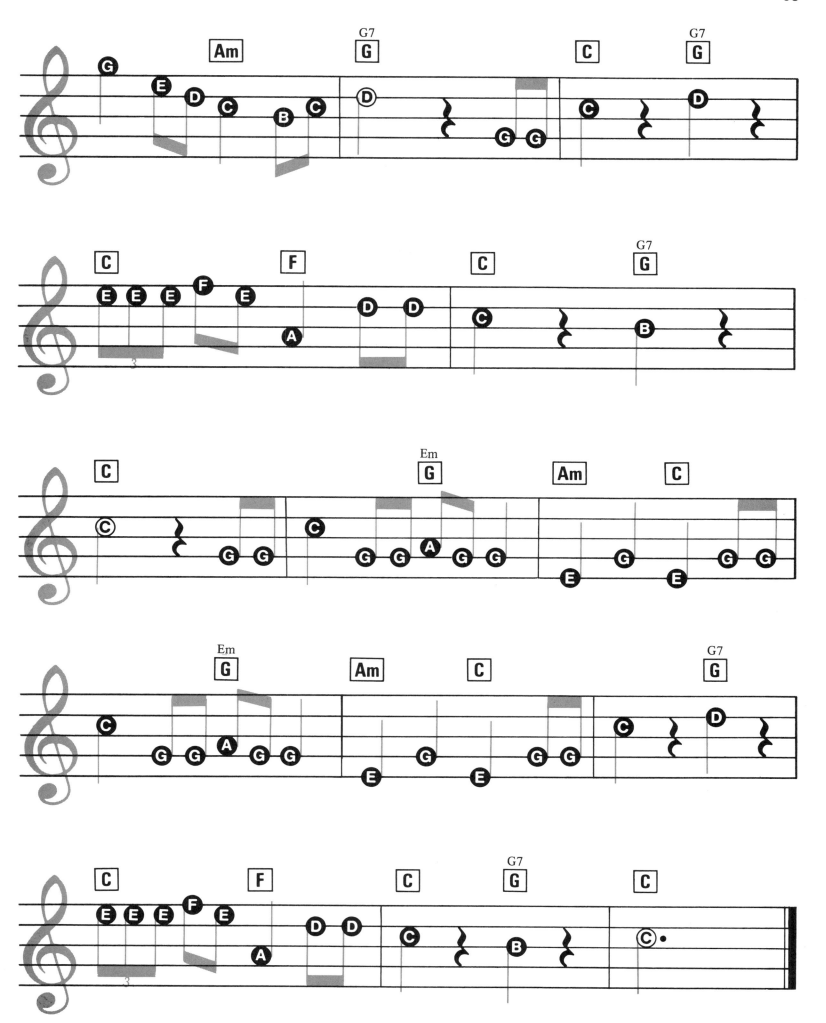

Yakety Sax (Axe)

Registration: *BRIGHT 'N BRASSY*

If using a "Sax" registration
activate Glide as indicated by ✳.

By James Rich
and Randy Randolph

97

Happy Together

Registration: *FULL 'N' BRILLIANT*

Words and Music by
Garry Bonner and Alan Gordon

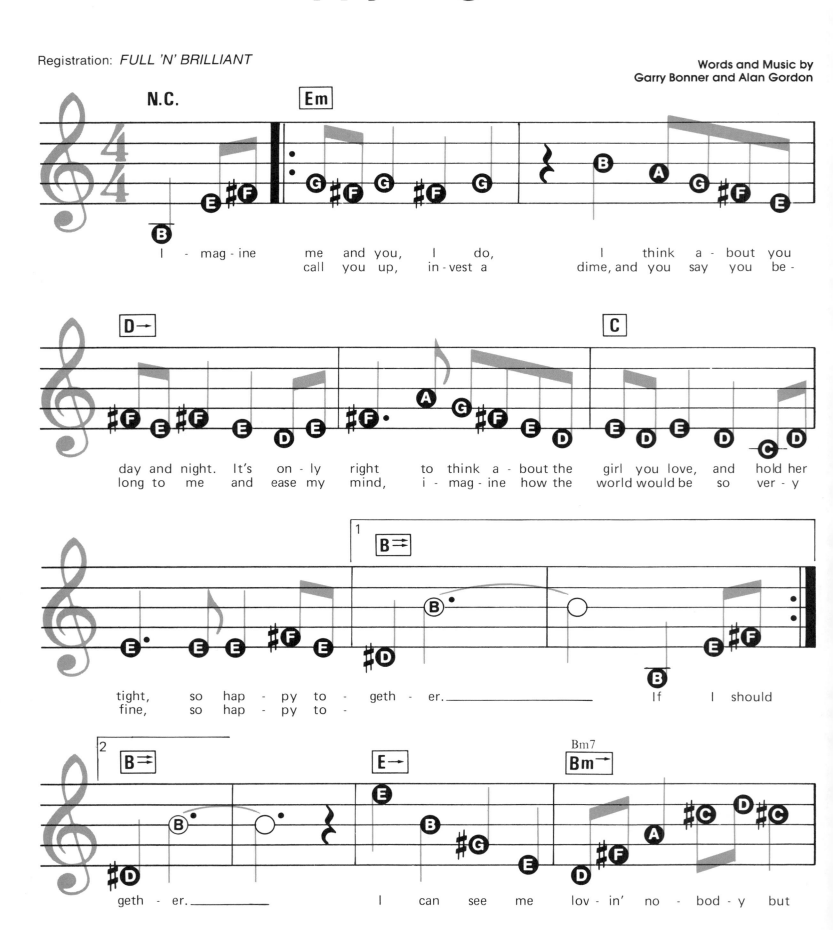

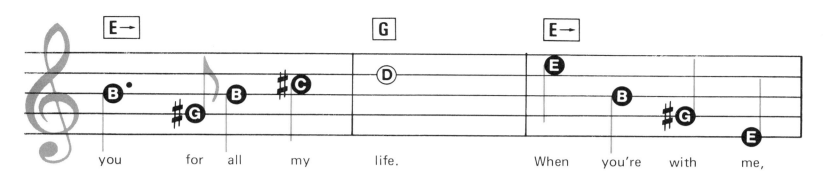

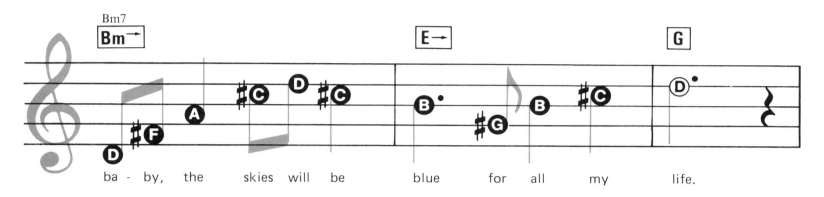

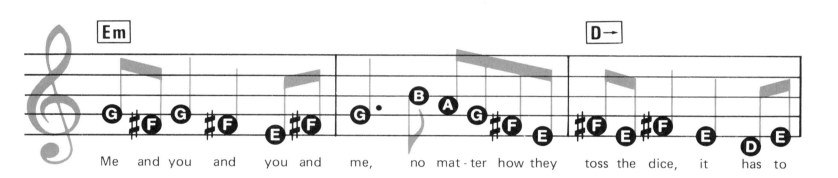

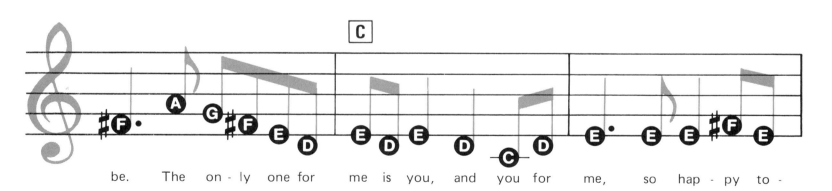

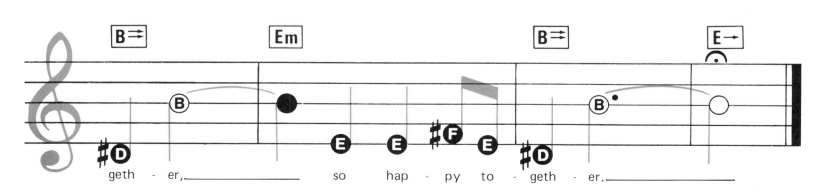

April Showers

120

Registration: *FULL 'N' MELLOW*

Words by B.G. DeSylva
Music by Louis Silvers

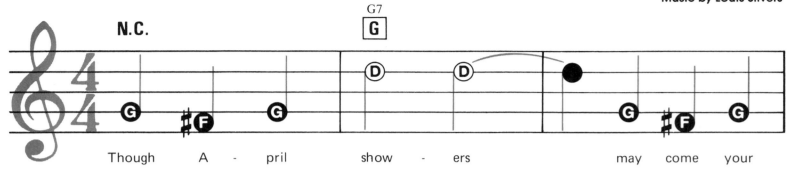

Though A - pril show - ers may come your

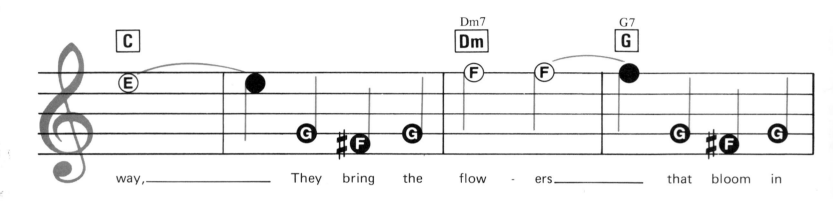

way,_____ They bring the flow - ers_____ that bloom in

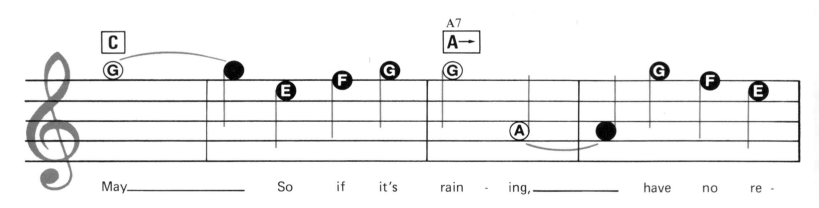

May_____ So if it's rain - ing,_____ have no re -

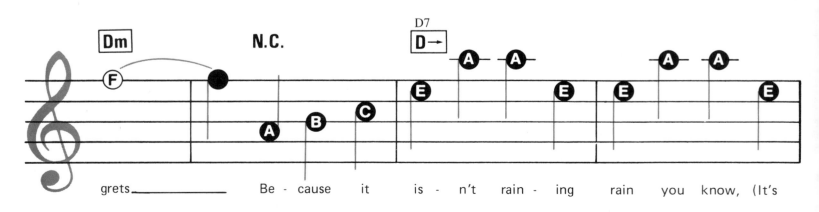

grets_____ Be - cause it is - n't rain - ing rain you know, (It's

101

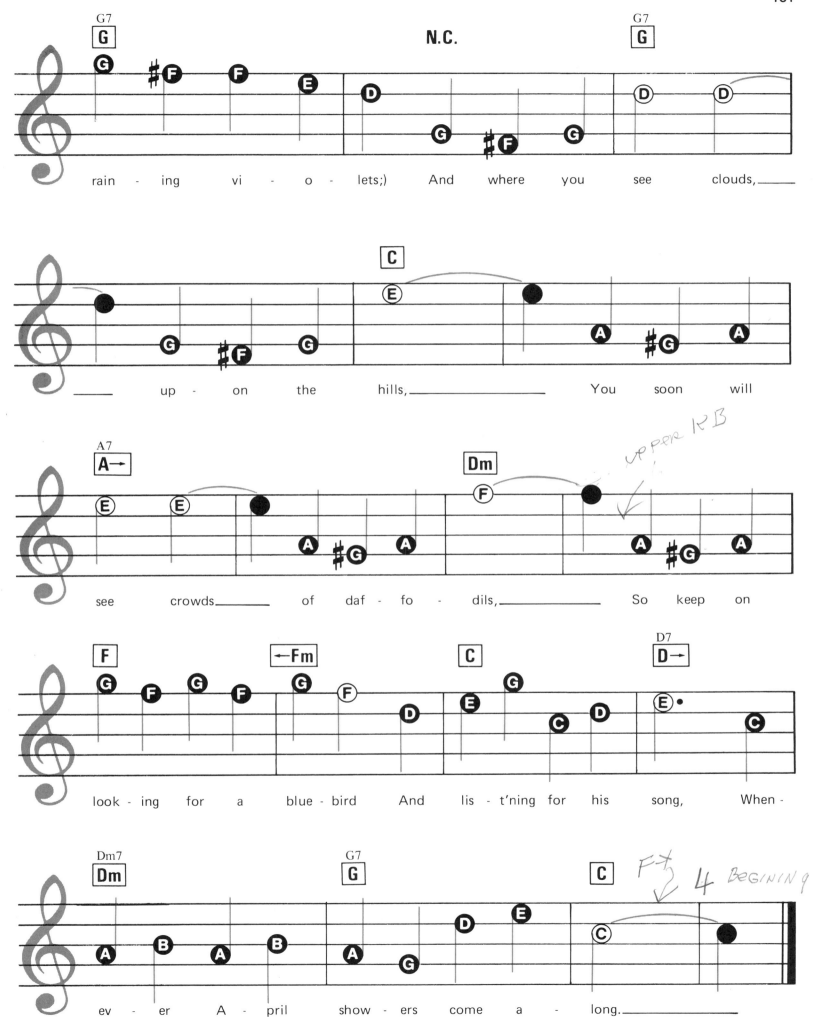

Indiana
(Back Home Again In Indiana)

Registration: *BRILLIANT SOLO*

Words by Ballard MacDonald
Music by James F. Hanley

103

CHORD SPELLER
STANDARD CHORD INVERSIONS

All chords are shown in their most commonly used inversions (positions). Other inversions may be used at any time to simplify changing chords.

CHORD FAMILY Abbrev.	MAJOR	MINOR (m)	AUGMENTED (aug)	7TH (7)	MINOR 7TH (m7)	DIMINISHED (dim)
C	G-C-E	G-C-E♭	G♯-C-E	G-B♭-C-E	G-B♭-C-E♭	G♭-A-C-E♭
D♭	A♭-D♭-F	A♭-D♭-E	A-D♭-F	A♭-B-D♭-F	A♭-B-D♭-E	G-B♭-D♭-E
D	F♯-A-D	A-D-F	F♯-A♯-D	F♯-A-C-D	A-C-D-F	A♭-B-D-F
E♭	G-B♭-E♭	G♭-B♭-E♭	G-B-E♭	G-B♭-D♭-E♭	G♭-B♭-D♭-E♭	G♭-A-C-E♭
E	G♯-B-E	G-B-E	G♯-C-E	G♯-B-D-E	G-B-D-E	G-B♭-D♭-E
F	A-C-F	A♭-C-F	A-C♯-F	A-C-E♭-F	A♭-C-E♭-F	A♭-B-D-F
F♯	F♯-A♯-C♯	F♯-A-C♯	F♯-A♯-D	F♯-A♯-C♯-E	F♯-A-C♯-E	F♯-A-C-E♭
G	G-B-D	G-B♭-D	G-B-D♯	G-B-D-F	G-B♭-D-F	G-B♭-D♭-E
A♭	A♭-C-E♭	A♭-B-E♭	A♭-C-E	A♭-C-E♭-G♭	A♭-B-E♭-G♭	A♭-B-D-F
A	A-C♯-E	A-C-E	A-C♯-F	G-A-C♯-E	G-A-C-E	F♯-A-C-E♭
B♭	B♭-D-F	B♭-D♭-F	F♯-B♭-D	A♭-B♭-D-F	A♭-B♭-D♭-F	G-B♭-D♭-E
B	F♯-B-D♯	F♯-B-D	G-B-D♯	F♯-A-B-D♯	F♯-A-B-D	A♭-B-D-F